THE STORY OF
Geronimo

*It seemed certain the two stallions must
close with each other*

Weekly Reader Books presents

THE STORY OF
Geronimo

By JIM KJELGAARD

Illustrated by CHARLES BANKS WILSON

ENID LAMONTE MEADOWCROFT
Supervising Editor

PUBLISHERS Grosset & Dunlap NEW YORK

PRINTED IN THE UNITED STATES OF AMERICA
Library of Congress Catalog Card No. 58–9837
The Story of Geronimo

For
ELEANOR GEFROH
who has been the dearest of friends
to me and mine

Contents

[*vii*]

Illustrations

THE STORY OF
Geronimo

CHAPTER ONE

Duel by Stallion

GERONIMO crawled up the hill so carefully that no stalk of grass moved, and no bush quivered. A pair of crested quail, feeding on insects in the grass, merely glanced up when he passed and went on feeding. Geronimo reached the top of the hill and crouched down in the grass.

Beyond were more hills, the near ones low, rocky, and given more to shrubs and grass than to trees. Geronimo's eyes strayed across the Arizona landscape to the east. There lay No-doyohn Canyon, where Geronimo had been born in 1829, just twelve years earlier. There his father had died when Geronimo was five years old. In the far distance beyond the canyon, tall, pine-clad mountains rose.

Geronimo looked down the slope on a wickiup. This Apache house was built of poles thrust into the ground, with deer skin walls and a smoke hole in the center of the roof. It was the home of Delgadito, a mighty chief among the Mimbreno Apaches, the tribe to which Geronimo belonged. Delgadito was so mighty that only the great chief, Mangus Coloradus himself, outranked him.

Delgadito owned many horses. Most of them grazed by day in pastures far from the village. But his black war stallion, his nimble-footed gray hunting horse, and the mare that his wife rode were only absent from their picket ropes when a rider was using them.

Now the gray hunting horse was gone, which meant that Delgadito was out after deer. But the mare and the stallion were still

there. Geronimo had come to steal the war
horse. This, however, was not the time to do
it.

The mare's presence proved that Delgadito's wife was home. If she saw Geronimo
stealing the war horse she would tell her hus-
band. The punishment sure to follow would
be harsh and long remembered. Delgadito
knew how to use a switch on headstrong boys.
Geronimo crouched in his hiding place, waiting.

Soon Delgadito's wife came from the wickiup, mounted her mare, and rode away. Geronimo rose and walked swiftly down the hill.
The stallion raised its head and watched

with eyes that were fearless and questioning. Geronimo grasped the buckskin tie rope, and was drawing the horse to him when---

"You leave my uncle's war horse alone!"

A girl had come from the wickiup. Geronimo was so interested in the horse that he did not even know she was near until she spoke. Her name was Alope, and she was Delgadito's niece. Geronimo thought she was so lovely that the most dazzling maidens of the Mimbreno or any other tribe were drab beside her. When grown, such a girl would be too good for any warrior. Only a chief would be worthy to have her as his wife.

Geronimo said, "I must have this stallion, Alope."

"Why?" Alope asked.

"I must fight a duel of stallions with Ponce, the son of Ponce, and the only stallion among my mother's horses is too old to fight," Geronimo said.

Alope asked, "Why must you fight such a duel with young Ponce?"

"He gave me the lie!" Geronimo said angrily. "I killed three deer with my bow and arrows. Ponce said I *found* them dead!"

"Twelve-year-old boys are not supposed to be able to kill deer," Alope said.

"I did!" Geronimo insisted.

"I believe you," Alope said. "But these duels are dangerous. You know the elders have forbidden them."

Geronimo patted the stallion's cheek.

"If the elders do not know a duel is being fought," he said, "they can do nothing."

"And if my uncle's war horse is killed," Alope told him, "he'll stake you out on an ant hill and let the ants devour you."

Geronimo said, "I'll gladly accept any punishment after I have fought this duel, but I must fight!"

"What if you are killed?" asked Alope.

"I won't be. Among all his father's horses, the son of Ponce shall find no stallion to equal this one, and I am a much better rider!"

Alope said, "My good sense bids me run and get my aunt, but my heart tells me to speed a warrior on his way. I'll not tell, but I'll tremble for what will happen to you should my uncle's war horse be killed or hurt."

Geronimo slipped the tether rope, grasped the rein, and vaulted happily to the back of the mighty horse. Though the stallion wanted to gallop and Geronimo burned to test the speed and fire of such a mount, he held him to a walk. There was a fight coming up. The stallion must go into it rested.

At the same time, it was a glorious feeling just to be on such a stallion. All Apaches could ride, but few were master horsemen. Geronimo had started riding the village colts when he was so small that it was necessary to lead his mount beside a boulder or stump from which he could scramble onto its back. He seemed born to ride. Not half a dozen men in the village could stay on the back of Delgadito's war horse. But Geronimo was riding him.

After twenty minutes the Indian boy looked down on the secluded swale where the duel would be fought. He and Ponce had chosen a battle ground far enough from the village so that the elders would be unlikely to interfere. Young Ponce was waiting there with one of his father's best horses, a fiery bay that had already slain a half dozen rivals.

Though the elders knew nothing of the duel, a crowd of boys ringed the chosen arena. They were tense with excitement, but they did not yell and shout as white boys would have. And all stood far enough away so that they could escape if either stallion charged toward them.

As Geronimo rode down the hill, Delgadito's war horse caught scent of the other stallion and screamed his challenge. Ponce's bay answered, and the two stallions rushed each other. Quickly Geronimo planned his battle.

Such duels were a common way for Apache boys to settle arguments. They often resulted in the death of a horse, a rider, or both. When they did, it was usually the rider's fault. Geronimo planned on using his riding skill to make a fool of Ponce, and he intended that nobody should get hurt.

Just as it seemed certain the two stallions must close with each other, Geronimo turned Delgadito's war horse so expertly that they passed within inches. At this wonderful display of riding skill, an excited murmur of admiration rose from the watching boys.

Geronimo turned back, this time wheeling right in front of Ponce's angry stallion. He swerved to come in to the side. Ponce's bay reared and pawed the air with skull-crushing front hoofs. The watching boys gasped. But just as it seemed certain that Geronimo would be killed, he leaned over and escaped by the width of a hair.

Suddenly, to Geronimo's vast surprise,

Ponce wheeled his stallion and galloped away as fast as his bay could run. Deciding to chase him on Delgadito's war horse, Geronimo was even more astonished when a shrill whistle split the air.

The war horse whirled and trotted obediently to—Delgadito himself! For the first time Geronimo noticed that the watching boys had disappeared too. He alone had been so interested in the duel that he had failed to see Delgadito come. The chief's eyes blazed with anger.

"Why do you fight a duel of stallions?" he demanded.

"The son of Ponce gave me the lie!" said Geronimo, sitting erect on the war horse. "I killed three deer with my bow and arrows! Young Ponce said I found them dead!"

"Come with me!" commanded Delgadito.

He turned toward his gray hunting horse, which was rein-haltered near by and which had a buck strapped behind the saddle. Without a word or a backward glance the tall chief mounted and rode at a walk in the direction of his wickiup.

Though he shivered inwardly, Geronimo did his best not to show it as he followed. Nor was he sorry that he had stolen the war horse.

He had acted as a warrior should; he would take his punishment like a warrior.

When they reached the wickiup, they dismounted and Delgadito tethered both horses. Then he removed his bow and quiver of ar-

rows from the hunting horse, took a single arrow from the quiver, and gave the arrow and the bow to Geronimo.

"Killer of deer, I would see you shoot," the chief ordered.

Geronimo fingered the unfamiliar weapon. "What target?"

Delgadito nodded at a pine about twenty yards away. "The knothole."

Geronimo nocked the arrow, raised the bow, and needed every ounce of his strength to draw it. This was a man's weapon, with a much heavier pull than the bow he had made for himself. But he did not shoot until he knew he was on target.

The arrow's shaft quivered as its copper point bit deeply into the knothole.

Delgadito said, "I saw you ride, and now I have seen you shoot. You told no lies. When the sun has risen three times more, I will lead a raid against the Papagoes, for we should steal more horses. You will ride with us."

Delgadito turned and entered his wickiup to indicate that Geronimo was dismissed. But for a full two minutes the dazed youngster did not move. At last, at long last, his fondest dream was coming true.

He was to be a true warrior.

CHAPTER TWO

Raiding the Papagoes

THREE DAYS later, at sunrise, an excited
Geronimo sat nervously on his mother's ag-
ing stallion and waited for the raiders to start.
Besides Delgadito, who was the leader, and
Geronimo, there were four braves named
Nadeze, Sanchez, Tacon, and Chie.

The dome-shaped wickiups where the vil-
lagers lived were softly beautiful in the early
morning light. Here and there the embers of
last night's cooking fire—for in this fine
spring weather the Apaches did most of their
cooking out of doors—glowed like a star
fallen to earth. But except for the sentries
who had been up all night, and the raiders
about to set forth, the village slept.

When all the raiders were mounted, Nadeze and Sanchez left the others. Presently
they returned driving a dozen loose horses

among which was a beautiful spotted apaloosa. This horse had belonged to a *shaman,* or medicine man, of the White Mountain Apaches and had been taken from him in a night raid.

It was always necessary to have extra horses when going into enemy country for any reason. They could serve as remounts. If there was no other food they could be eaten, or they could be traded if there were any opportunities for trading.

But Geronimo wondered why Nadeze and Sanchez had included the apaloosa. The spotted horse was famous throughout the land. Even the Papagoes and pueblo-dwelling Zuñi knew him, and whoever saw him would surely send winged words to the *shaman.*

"Then a war party from the White Mountain Apaches will come to rescue their medicine man's horse," Geronimo thought. But he asked no questions. Surely Delgadito knew what he was doing.

Nadeze and Sanchez drove the loose horses on at full gallop, for the sooner the animals were tired the sooner they would be willing to stay with the rest and the less trouble they would cause. The other raiders rode out from the village more slowly.

[14]

An hour later they overtook Nadeze and Sanchez, and the driven horses, now too tired to run. They fell in at the rear and seemed satisfied to stay there. Geronimo felt a rising anxiety.

He had always imagined raiding to be a stealthy business. These men laughed, shouted, and gaily mimicked a coyote that moaned from a nearby ridge.

Presently lithe, slim Tacon challenged fat Chie to a race. Whooping at the tops of their voices, they were off. Geronimo stopped worrying. Delgadito was too experienced a raider to do anything foolish. If he let the warriors act as though there were no enemies within twenty miles, then there were none.

That night they camped on top of a rocky hill from which they could see in all directions, and they were careful to put all fires out as soon as darkness fell.

"Fire may be seen for a long distance on a dark night," Geronimo said to himself. "That is why they were put out."

The next morning the raiders rode on, and not until midafternoon did they make the slightest attempt to hide themselves. But when they finally halted under a cloud-ridden sky, there was a change in every man.

This was desert country, and they stopped in a cluster of rocky hills. Delgadito and Chie dismounted and climbed the tallest hill to scout from its summit. Soon they returned and told the others to dismount too. Tether ropes were slipped about the necks of the loose horses, which were now led by the raiders as all went on quietly.

A half hour later the raiders made a second stop in a dry wash. The banks of this desert creek bed were about four feet high and rimmed by cactus and palo verde trees.

Sanchez and Delgadito felled one of these trees with copper hatchets, cut off two stout chunks, and tied either end of a long rawhide thong to them. Then they stretched the thong as far as it would reach, and buried the chunks in the earth, at the bottom of the creek bed. Careful to place a gentle horse between two quick-tempered mounts, they tied all animals to this picket line. This done, all got their weapons and started up over the wash.

Geronimo ran happily for his own bow and arrows and followed. Suddenly Delgadito turned, put the palm of his hand against the youngster's face, and pushed so hard that Geronimo found himself seated in the bottom of the wash.

"Stay here to watch the horses," the chief growled.

"But I'm a warrior too!" Geronimo protested.

Delgadito growled again, and amused smiles flitted over the lips of the others. The raiders melted into the desert.

Flames of anger scorched Geronimo's cheeks, and rage ate at his heart. He had a fierce desire to pursue and kill Delgadito in revenge for being knocked down. But he knew that he must obey his chief. And he found it much more satisfactory to be guarding warriors' horses than to be playing children's games in the village.

Geronimo pillowed his back against a

boulder and for a while never took his eyes
from the horses. Then it began to seem foolish to watch them at all. The animals were
standing quietly, and the idea that an enemy
might come into the creek bed seemed unlikely. Presently Geronimo went to sleep.

Some time later he awakened. At first he
thought he had been disturbed by the deep-
ening clouds and a feeling that rain would
soon fall. Then he peered down the wash.

Two nearly naked Indians carrying war
clubs were stalking the horses and were only
about forty yards from the nearest animal.
Their clubs, the way they wore their straight
black hair, and their tattooed faces stamped
them as Papagoes. It was plain to see that they
intended to steal the horses.

When he was certain that neither Papago
was looking in his direction, Geronimo slung
his quiver of arrows over his back. Taking his
bow in hand, he crawled swiftly to and under
the nearest horse.

The horses were not in an even line, but
all stood perfectly still because they were interested in the Papagoes, and their legs
formed a rough tunnel. Geronimo crawled
down it. Reaching the last horse, he stopped
and licked dry lips.

*The Papagoes saw him, raised their clubs
and rushed forward*

He wished Delgadito or any of the others were there. It was one thing to dream of becoming a warrior and quite another to face the enemy. What should he do now? Then the Papagoes saw him, raised their clubs and rushed forward, and there was only one thing he could do.

Geronimo plucked an arrow from his quiver, nocked it, drew his bow, took careful aim at the nearest Papago, and shot. The Papago was hit squarely in the heart. The only sound as the man fell was a jarring thud when he struck the ground. His companion turned to run.

Forgetting to nock another arrow, Geronimo crawled weakly from beneath the horse and for a few minutes sat shivering. Then he remembered that, though he was still a boy, he would soon be not just a warrior but an Apache warrior. Forcing himself to rise, he walked over to look at the dead Papago, and told himself that he was glad he had put an end to another enemy of the Apache. But he was just as happy that he had not killed the second Papago too.

Before long a black horse, flanked by a gray and four bays, jumped down into the wash, ran across it, and stopped. They stared back in the direction from which they had come, and the tethered horses raised their heads to stare too. Geronimo thought that the black was a wonderful stallion and was surely stolen from some Mexican *rancheria* because no Papagoes bred horses so fine.

Now more horses came galloping over the desert until there was a herd of about eighty milling around in the wash. For the most part they were scrawny Papago ponies. But Geronimo saw one more fine stallion, a dark gray with black spots.

Riding stolen ponies, which they guided without help of saddle or bridle, Delgadito and his raiders were on the heels of the last horses. As their mounts jumped into the wash they slid off. Delgadito made his way to Geronimo and looked down at the dead Papago.

"How is this?" the chief asked.

"He would have stolen our horses," Geronimo replied.

"Was he alone?"

"There was another," the boy admitted. "I did not kill him."

"You should have," Delgadito scolded. "But come now and mount."

Geronimo ran with him to the picket line

and mounted his mother's old stallion, then
he was astounded to see Delgadito take time
to strip saddle and bridle from his own horse
and put them on the apaloosa. Geronimo
marveled. This was enemy country and,
when the Papagoes discovered that some of
their horses had been stolen, they were sure
to launch a hot pursuit. But Delgadito
seemed as calm as he had ever been at home
in his own wickiup.

Mounting the apaloosa and whooping at the top of his voice, Delgadito charged the herd. The other riders took off, one after another, and drove the horses full speed straight north. This puzzled Geronimo. Finally he rode over to talk with Nadeze.

"Why do we go north?" he asked. "Our home is almost due east."

"Worry not and question not," Nadeze said coolly. "Look and learn."

Always at full gallop, Delgadito was racing from one end of the line to the other. The apaloosa already had run at least six times the distance any other horse had traveled.

About an hour and a half later Delgadito caught his own horse and transferred saddle and bridle from the apaloosa to him. The exhausted apaloosa staggered ten feet to stand with head drooping. Geronimo finally understood.

Beyond any doubt, Papago trackers were already on the trail of Delgadito's Mimbreno raiders. They could not fail to find the weary apaloosa and they would know its owner was the *shaman* of the White Mountain Apaches. They would also see that the stolen horses had been started northward, toward the home of these Apaches. Thus the Papagoes would think that they had been raided by men from the White Mountain tribe and they would seek revenge on them, rather than on the Mimbreno Apaches.

"We have a wise chief," thought Geronimo, as Delgadito's plan became clear to him.

Just then Delgadito said, "Chie, continue northward with thirty of the more worthless horses. Leave a plain trail, as though we were stricken with panic. But drive the horses back and forth so it will appear as though there were many more than thirty. Run as soon as you see pursuers."

Chie nodded, and the rest of the men started dividing the remaining horses into smaller groups.

"Why do we do this?" Geronimo asked, riding along beside Nadeze.

"It is easier to hide the trail of a small group of horses," said Nadeze. "And the Papagoes will find it much more difficult to track us since we will take each herd in a different direction before swinging back to our village."

"Do I drive some?"

"You are too anxious, stripling." Nadeze was far more respectful since Geronimo had slain the Papago. "You will ride with one of us."

Suddenly the rain clouds which Geronimo had noticed earlier loosed an earth-battering torrent. The raiders smiled. Usan, god of their tribe, had indeed blessed them. Though the Papago trackers would certainly find the apaloosa, they would never discover where the rest of the horses had gone after a storm such as this one.

Driving all the horses ahead of them

through the pouring rain, the raiders turned homeward.

In bright sunlight next day, the stolen Papago horses cropped grass on the slope opposite Delgadito's wickiup. Geronimo listened anxiously while Delgadito, as was the right of a chief who led a raiding party, divided the plunder.

The leader reserved twenty horses for himself, and the twenty he chose included the two fine stallions. Then he gave smaller numbers of horses to the four men who had gone with him. The number each received depended on how hard he had worked to make the raid successful. Next came a just share for all families who had no one to steal horses for them.

Geronimo's heart sank as the horses were given away. He had hoped to get something for himself, but now the only horses remaining were a dozen or so fit only for the cooking pot. Delgadito declared them as such. Then he announced, so that all could hear:

"I give part of my portion, the black stallion and the gray stallion with black spots," he swung to Geronimo, "to an Apache youth who deserves them because during this raid he behaved like a warrior."

For a moment Geronimo was too surprised and delighted to move. Then he tilted his head, squared his shoulders, and went proudly forth to claim his prizes.

CHAPTER THREE

Alope

IT WAS spring in the year 1846, five years after Geronimo's first raid. Ten miles south of the Arizona-Mexico border, Geronimo sat silently on the summit of a low hill. His knife was on his belt. His muzzle-loading rifle, powder horn, and bullet pouch were in easy reach. A red blanket was draped over his body, which was naked except for breech cloth, moccasins, and the warrior's head-band that bound his black hair.

Two young warriors, Zayigo and Pedro Gonzalez, sat beside him. Both were older than Geronimo. Yet both had chosen to let the seventeen-year-old warrior lead this raid into Mexico because of his cunning and courage.

Now they were a little uneasy because of their leader's silence. Usually Geronimo loved to talk, and he was already a leading orator among the Mimbreno Apaches. When

he was least talkative, he was most dangerous.
Finally Zayigo said impatiently:

"We sit beside the youngest Mimbreno
Apache ever to become a member of the
Council of Warriors. Yet he sulks like a
scolded child. It ill befits him."

"Aye," Pedro Gonzalez agreed. "Since leaving the Mimbreno village, Geronimo, you
have smoldered like a fire that is not quite

able to burst into flame. Is it because some warriors spoke against you when they met to determine whether you might be admitted to the Council?"

"I care not who speaks against me," Geronimo said sourly. "Any who consider me unworthy of being a Mimbreno warrior I'll fight gladly."

"Those who did not want to admit you to the Council of Warriors never questioned your bravery or your skill in battle," Zayigo said quickly. "They said only that you are reckless and headstrong, and that trouble goes where you do because you never reckon the odds."

"There are some Mimbreno warriors who have the cowardly souls of Mexicans," Geronimo grunted. "And I do not mean that you are a coward, Pedro."

Pedro Gonzalez said quietly, "Mexican I was once. Apache I am now."

That was true. Captured in Mexico when he was five years old, Pedro had been adopted by an Apache family. He had taken so readily to Apache ways that he was now one of their finest and fiercest warriors. He spoke again:

"If you care not because some spoke against you, what is the trouble? It is no pleasure to go raiding or anywhere else with one who does little except stew in his own anger."

Geronimo said bitterly, "Ne-po-se was one of the men who spoke against me."

"The father of Alope does not like you," Zayigo said. "But that is no news in the Mimbreno village. Ne-po-se does not care to have Alope marry a mere warrior when it is possible that a chief will offer five horses in exchange for her."

For a moment Geronimo did not answer. For five years he had watched Alope become lovelier each year. Her image accompanied him wherever he went by day and haunted his dreams by night. He was as deeply in love as a young man can be.

He said finally, "When I became a warrior in full standing, I went to Ne-po-se and asked for Alope. He sneered at me, and said to come back when I could offer ten horses for his daughter's hand."

"Ten horses!" Zayigo said in astonishment. "That is unheard of, even for such a bride as Alope! What do you intend to do?"

"Pay for my bride what she is worth," Geronimo said. "That is why we are in Mexico, where there are plenty of horses for the taking."

[*31*]

He spoke more easily, for talking about his troubles had made them seem less. Zayigo and Pedro Gonzalez smiled, their white teeth flashing in the darkness.

"Now you talk as the leader we hoped we were following," Pedro Gonzalez said happily. "Of course there are plenty of horses in Mexico. And when it comes to stealing horses, no warriors are more clever than Geronimo. You shall gain the price of your bride."

"I shall have the price or I shall not return to the Mimbreno village," Geronimo vowed. "And I know we shall return for we go against Mexicans.

"I think it must be true that something in the food they eat or the water they drink turns the marrow of Mexican men's bones to jelly as soon as they become men. Captive Mexican women fit very well into our tribe, as do children if taken young enough. The men do little except tremble with fear, and that is why it is better to kill than capture them."

Pedro Gonzalez laughed joyously. "It is long since I have fought Mexicans. Let us hope this is a good fight."

They curled up in their blankets and slept. The night was still black about them when they rose to go on. Traveling at a loose-legged gait that covered the ground with amazing speed, they were many miles from their camping place when the sun rose. They stopped to nibble parched corn from pouches that hung at their belts, rested less than five minutes, and went on.

Geronimo, who had been this way many times and who also had a splendid sense of direction, led the others through steep-walled canyons and over brush-grown hilltops. By midafternoon they were looking from the top of a hill down on the *rancheria* they intended to raid.

The house and other buildings were built of adobe, or sun-dried brick. To one side were extensive corrals made of poles that had been laboriously hauled from some river bottom or other where trees were plentiful. There were about fifty horses in the corrals.

The three Apaches crouched in the brush and bided their time. They were heedless of the sun that burned down upon them. Thirst that would have driven a white man mad bothered them not at all. They were trained to endure thirst.

An hour before dark, several Mexican riders came with a herd of forty horses. They put them in the same corral where the fifty were already confined, and turned their own saddle mounts in with them. Two more riders came, stripped saddles and bridles from their mounts, and shut them in the corral. Then all the Mexicans went into the house.

Night fell before the three Apaches stirred. Geronimo gave his orders.

"Zayigo and Pedro, keep those in the house from coming out. I go to the corral."

Geronimo slipped away in the darkness. He could no longer see the corral, but his sense of direction was so sure that he went exactly to it. The Mexicans had draped their saddles over the top rail and hung their bridles on the saddle horns. Taking no saddles, for all three raiders were expert bareback riders, Geronimo looped three bridles over his shoulder and entered the corral.

The horses snorted in alarm when they got his scent, then wheeled to run to the corral's far side. Geronimo did not hurry even slightly, for in the first place any quick move would frighten the horses. In the second place, with Zayigo and Pedro Gonzalez watching the house, he was not afraid that the Mexicans would come. In the third place, Geronimo had done this so many times that he knew exactly how to go about it.

The horses snorted in alarm

Presently he backed a group of horses into a corner of the corral. Geronimo caught one, held it by looping the reins of one of his three bridles around its neck, and bridled it. He mounted.

At that moment, a stallion screamed.

The door of the house was flung open. But when Zayigo's rifle spoke, the door was slammed shut quickly. Still refusing to hurry, Geronimo caught and bridled two more horses. Sitting his own mount, and holding the reins of the other two, he whistled shrilly.

Zayigo and Pedro Gonzalez appeared out of the darkness. Not speaking, for each knew exactly what he must do, they mounted the two bridled horses. Geronimo opened the gate and the three drove the herd through.

There were hundreds of other horses grazing on the vast acreage of the *rancheria*. But this was the only herd kept near the house and the raiders had been careful to take all of them. The rest were miles away at other water holes. Even if the Mexicans recovered their wits immediately, they would still need hours to get more horses and launch any kind of pursuit.

The raiders drove their herd toward Apache land at a leisurely walk.

Geronimo brought the skins of puma

On their return Geronimo gave Ne-po-se twenty fine horses. It was a gift so dazzling that even Mangus Coloradus, giant chief of the Mimbreno Apaches, came to inquire about it. And Ne-po-se could no longer forbid Alope to marry the brave young Geronimo.

Several thousand people lived in the Mimbreno village. But since most Apaches liked plenty of room between themselves and their neighbors, the village was spread over several hills.

Geronimo and Alope, however, built a fine wickiup very near the house of Geronimo's widowed mother. Alope decorated it with pictures while Geronimo brought the skins of elk, deer, antelope, puma, and other creatures that fell to his hunting arrows. There were no bear skins because bears are sacred to Apaches.

The following twelve years were probably the only truly happy ones Geronimo ever knew. A daughter came to live in the wickiup, then a son, then another daughter. It was a full and wonderful life for all.

CHAPTER FOUR

Massacre

AGAIN it was spring, the spring of 1858, and almost the entire village of Mimbreno Apaches was on the move.

Twenty or more youngsters, who couldn't contain their own bubbling spirits and wouldn't restrain their lively ponies, led the main column by half a mile. Next, riding his immense war horse and surrounded by his sub-chiefs, came Mangus Coloradus himself —a giant of a man and a great leader. Immediately behind this group were more than three hundred pack horses and burros. Their packs bore tanned skins, fruit of the saguaro cactus, edible roots of the mescal plant, and other trade goods.

The pack train was guarded by warriors who rode on either side. Far enough behind so that they would not be bothered too much by the dust of the pack train, came the remainder of the warriors, the old people, and the women and children. All were mounted. Some of the smaller children rode four or five to a pony. They were going on a holiday of the happiest sort.

Though the Apaches were usually at war with the Mexicans, they had arranged a peace so that they might have their great annual trading party, or *fiesta,* in Mexico. Most of their trading would be done in the town of

Casas Grandes, deep in the Mexican state of Chihuahua. But before reaching Casas Grandes they intended to stop and trade at a

smaller town which they called Kas-Kai-Ya.

Two and a half miles short of town they halted and set up camp. This was a simple enough business. Most of the Indians just cast their blankets down on the ground and arranged a fireplace. Some cut green saplings and thrust the thick ends in the ground to form a circle. Next they bent the tops together and held them with buckskin thongs. Then they thatched the walls with deer skins or blankets.

Geronimo started building such a wickiup for his mother, Alope, and his three children. His two daughters, ten and five, and his seven-year-old son tried so enthusiastically to help him that the wickiup never would have been built if Alope hadn't taken charge.

The Apaches had not stopped so far from Kas-Kai-Ya because they were afraid of the Mexicans. But, though Mexican women might roam at will in Apache villages, no Apache woman would think of showing herself in a Mexican town. Besides, trading was a man's business.

Leaving enough warriors to protect a peaceful camp, the eighty men who were going in town to trade set out, led by Mangus Coloradus himself. They took only thirty horses, twelve of which were laden with trade goods. The rest of the trade goods and the pack horses and burros were saved for trading in Casas Grandes.

Every warrior except Geronimo had a hidden knife. Some carried hidden pistols, and a few had carbines, or short rifles, thrust inside their breeches. To enter the town openly armed would surely provoke a fight, and a fight would spoil the holiday. But even though they were supposedly at peace, no Apache ever trusted any Mexican and no Mexican ever trusted any Apache.

Geronimo carried only a buckskin pouch

filled with yellow metal that, to him, hadn't
the slightest value. Made into arrow or lance
heads, it blunted on almost any target. It was
too heavy for hair or ear ornaments, and use-
less to the Apaches except as playthings for
the children. But the Mexicans, who called
the metal *oro*—gold—prized it greatly.

The traders reached the sun-dried brick
wall enclosing the town of Kas-Kai-Ya and
found a squadron of *rurales* drawn in formation across the gate. All these soldier police
were mounted and armed, and their snapping
black eyes were filled with hatred for Apaches.
As Geronimo knew, there was good reason
for this hate. Apaches had raided too long,
too often, and too successfully in Mexico to
win any friendship from *rurales* whose duty
it was to stop them. Mangus Coloradus addressed the uniformed officer:

"*Buenas tardes, Señor Rurale.* We would
trade."

The officer made an effort to stare Mangus
Coloradus down, and when he couldn't do it,
flushed angrily. But he replied civilly:

"*Buenas tardes,* good afternoon, Señor
Apache. You may enter."

The *rurales* drew aside, let the Apaches
through the gate, and then reformed across

[*43*]

it. The Apaches braced themselves to meet the horde of peddlers that screeched and squawked down on them.

Geronimo was confronted by a lanky man whose only garment was a tattered *serape,* or blanket-like robe, that was draped over one shoulder and pinned at the sides with thorns. His hair looked as though it hadn't been combed in years, his beard was as tangled. His body was dirty. His eyes were both cunning and humble.

In sharp contrast were the fierce eyes of a golden eagle that the Mexican had imprisoned in a wooden cage. In spite of broken and bedraggled feathers, the eagle still looked royal. The Mexican lifted the cage.

"See?" he whined. "See, Señor Apache? Grieved though I must be to part with anything so precious, this noble bird is yours for only three horses."

Geronimo brushed haughtily past the man and walked on. The peddler called anxiously, "Will you give me some mescal?"

Geronimo's eyes expressed his disgust. If wild things were not meant for the wilds, the god, Usan, would not have placed them there. They might be hunted for food but never should any be imprisoned.

"Some tobacco?" the eagle's captor wailed. Geronimo turned, glared, and the Mexican scurried away. Geronimo continued his unhurried walk. Kas-Kai-Ya was truly remarkable, largely, Geronimo thought, because so many people could live in such a small area. They were so crowded that Geronimo wondered how they kept from suffocating each other.

He saw a man lying with his head on a chunk of adobe, the same sun-dried brick from which the town walls and all the buildings were fashioned. Suddenly the man leaped up and began to scream. Other Mexican men, women, even children at once started to scream or shout as loudly as they could. The clamor was deafening.

The amazed Apaches halted and gaped. After a bit, assuring himself that this senseless yelling must be a sickness suffered by those who allow themselves too little room, Geronimo went on.

Presently he halted beside a Mexican who had a basket supported by a ragged rope over one shoulder. The basket was divided into compartments and filled with glass beads that were separated according to color.

The beads were so fascinating that Geron-

He halted beside a Mexican

imo scarcely knew that the horrible din had quieted.

He caught up a half dozen assorted beads and one by one put them back in the proper compartments. He took out his pouch of gold. But though he yearned for the beads, and would gladly have given all his gold for them, he was too good a trader to offer everything at once. Geronimo dropped two small nuggets onto the palm of his hand and held them out.

"No," the bead vendor refused.

But excitement made him breathe hard, and he could not take his eyes from the pouch. Geronimo gave him two more nuggets. The Mexican gasped and Geronimo thought he was once more refusing. Recklessly he poured half the gold into the bead vendor's palm. The Mexican moaned, slipped the basket from his own shoulder and hung it on Geronimo's, cupped the gold with both hands, and ran.

Geronimo dropped the still half-filled pouch of gold into the dust and forgot it. He noticed for the first time that his comrades were making their way toward the gate. Trading had been brisk. The Apache trade goods were gone and each warrior had at least a double handful of knickknacks. The *rurales* drew their horses aside and let the departing Apaches through the gate.

The Indians started back to their camp. But when they were halfway there Mangus Coloradus halted suddenly. A split second later, every warrior was alert. From a brush-grown *arroyo,* or gully, came the hushed voice of Pedro Gonzalez, one of those who had stayed behind.

"This way."

The eighty melted into the *arroyo* as quietly as eighty quail might slip away from an approaching hunter. They found Nadeze with Pedro. The wives of five of the men who had gone into town and the wives of four who had stayed behind were there also. And two girl children. The faces of all showed shocked, numbing grief. But the eyes of all, even the two children, blazed with fury.

"Some *rurales* came!" Pedro snarled. "I know not from where! But they outnumbered us two to one. And when we warriors would have fought rather than let them enter the camp, they reminded us that this is a time of peace! They said they wished only to trade and talk, but once among us they attacked without warning! We slew many, but our horses, our arms, our trade goods, are now theirs! Of those men, women, and children who stayed behind, we alone live!"

"Where are the *rurales* now?" asked Mangus Coloradus.

"In what was our camp, awaiting your return," Pedro said.

Mangus Coloradus said, "When Apaches do not make fools of Mexicans, the Mexicans seem determined to make fools of themselves. The *rurales* must have known that some escaped, and that we would be warned. They should have ambushed us as we left the gates of Kas-Kai-Ya."

Sadly he thought of all who had been killed. Then he added "I will take the wives of our brave men and these two children with me, and I will hold myself responsible for their safety. Of the rest, each seek a different path and hide his trail. We will meet at the place we have chosen to be our rendezvous."

A moment later, the *arroyo* was empty of Apaches.

CHAPTER FIVE

Flight

LIGHT from a thin slice of moon glanced from the Bavispe River, stole through thinly leaved trees, and painted a lichen-crusted boulder with moonbeams.

But the moonlight made not the faintest impression in the grove of thick-limbed, heavy-trunked trees on the river's bank. Beneath the trees it was black enough for devils to dance. But any devils who might have been there would have been frightened away by the Apaches who had come to Mexico in peace but who knew now that there must be war. This grove was their appointed rendezvous should anything go amiss while they were trading.

Geronimo sat as though he had lost everything that made him alive but was still not dead. He knew dimly that Mangus Coloradus was talking in low tones with men whom Geronimo was too dazed to recognize.

The Mimbreno chief said, "We must go to our village."

"And leave our dead?" The question was laden with heartbreak.

Mangus Coloradus said, "We are deep in enemy country, with few arms, no food, and no horses. Is there another way?"

"I will not go," Nadeze said firmly.

"Then you will not return to meet again those who massacred our people," said the chief.

"Return?" Nadeze was puzzled.

"We will come again," Mangus Coloradus promised, "but with warriors only."

"Ha!" Nadeze snarled like an angry puma. "If my dead know that, they will forgive me for leaving! I must go and tell them!"

Others announced their intention to return to the encampment for one last visit with their dead.

"Go we may, but we must go cautiously and we must not linger," Mangus Coloradus said. "The *rurales* may still await us there. If they do not, the night is our friend. And we must ask our friend to shield us while we travel far."

A clear thought penetrated Geronimo's numbed brain. At the time when the massacre must have occurred, the people of Kas-Kai-Ya had set up a deafening racket. Why, if not to make it impossible for the warriors in town to hear rifle shots?

The thought faded and Geronimo was again a live body with a numbed brain and sick soul. He understood dully that they must return to their village, but that first they would have one last visit at the encampment. He rose only because the others did, and started out of the grove.

They found and traveled the trail to the Apache encampment. It was a bold move and, under a lesser chief than Mangus Coloradus, might have been disastrous. But the Mimbreno chief had rightly decided that Mexicans gauged Apache hearts by their own. If such a disaster had stricken Mexicans, the survivors would never have dared show themselves on the trail. Neither would they have visited the scene of the massacre.

When the angry and grief-stricken Apaches reached the encampment, they found that the *rurales* had left. The moon was merciful. The crumpled figures that lay all about seemed like so many sleeping persons.

Geronimo sought the wickiup where he had left his family.

He stopped suddenly. Alope lay full length before him, head turned and cheek resting on her right hand. Her long black hair tumbled at her side. Many times had Geronimo watched her sleep in just such a fashion, and now she seemed asleep. But she did not wake.

Geronimo's mother had fallen at the entrance to the wickiup, and the children were near. The two little girls had embraced when the Mexicans overtook them, and had fallen with their arms still about each other. The boy was at his sisters' feet. His right arm was stretched toward them, and he still clutched the rock which he had intended to throw at the treacherous Mexicans.

Geronimo was unaware of the hand that touched his arm, until Mangus Coloradus said gently, "Come with us, brother."

Geronimo responded like an obedient dog. He felt no grief, no shock, no pain, for he was too numbed to feel anything. He knew he must follow only because he had been told that he must.

By sunrise the Apaches were many miles from the scene of tragedy. Mangus Coloradus had led them over the roughest and rockiest places. They had waded streams wherever streams flowed and done everything possible to hide their trail.

At last Mangus Coloradus called a halt and sent some out to hunt while he told others to build a smokeless fire from dead wood. One by one, the hunters returned. Since a shot from a gun would have attracted attention, the game had been brought down with thrown rocks or knives. Their bag consisted of some jack rabbits and a crippled peccary. They ate, rested, and went on.

Geronimo remembered nothing of the flight. On reaching the village, he went first to his mother's wickiup. He entered, but at once ducked out again and sought his own house. Slowly the fogs faded from his brain.

He discovered that he still carried the basket of beads for which he had traded half a pouch of gold in Kas-Kai-Ya.

He had not realized, that night while the thin moon lighted the scene of the massacre, that the beloved people upon whom he looked were dead. Nor had he understood since. But he knew it now.

Geronimo plunged into his wickiup and sought his store of weapons. Shotguns, rifles, muskets, powder, shot, knives, hatchets, lances, bows, and arrows were carried a safe distance from the wickiup and put carefully down. The basket of beads was placed near them.

Then Geronimo strode to a nearby fire. Catching up a burning brand, he fired the wickiup he had shared with Alope, then cast the brand against his mother's house. He turned his back on the burning wickiups. Like his old life, they would soon be ashes. But there would be a new life, he told himself. A life of revenge!

Pedro Gonzalez was attracted to the fires, and Geronimo asked him, "Do you have weapons?"

"Bow and arrows, a knife, a lance, a hatchet."

Geronimo indicated his own store. "Choose what you will."

Pedro's brows arched in surprise. "You make gifts of such?"

"I give a weapon to whoever will ride with me and meet the *rurales* who murdered our people."

"I will ride, but only when Mangus Coloradus says to. He is still chief."

"Coward!" Geronimo spat.

Pedro's face tightened with anger, and he drew his knife. Geronimo grunted contemptuously and snatched at his own knife. Before either could make a thrust, Mangus Coloradus stepped between them.

"What insanity is this?" the chief thundered.

"I offered him his choice of weapons if he will return and fight the *rurales!*" Geronimo flared. "He will not go!"

"I will!" Pedro snapped. "But I wait until Mangus Coloradus leads!"

Mangus Coloradus whirled on Geronimo. "Have you turned fool?"

"I go to fight the murderers of my family," Geronimo said flatly.

"None of us has forgotten our dead," the chief replied. "We will go to avenge them, but to do so we must not only fight the Mexicans. We must defeat them. To defeat them, we must plan."

"Plan?" Geronimo inquired.

"We will seek Cochise, chief of the Chiricahua Apaches, and Whoa, chief of the Nedni," Mangus Coloradus said gravely. "We will ask their help. Then we will prepare. And then we will ride!"

CHAPTER SIX

Revenge

ALL fires in the camp near the Bavispe River had been extinguished before sundown. Naiche, the young, tall, courageous son of Cochise, sat in the darkness with Geronimo. Geronimo spoke.

"An autumn, a winter, and a spring have been born and died since Mangus Coloradus sent me as his spokesman to ask the help of the Chiricahuas and the Nedni."

"I well remember your visit," Naiche said. "When you spoke, your words were fire that burned into my very heart. As I listened I knew that, if no other Chiricahua would follow you to Mexico and help avenge the massacre of your people, Naiche would."

"Soon the battle," Geronimo said.

"Soon the battle," Naiche echoed. "And at last I shall know."

"What shall you know?"

"Why so mighty a warrior as Geronimo, who owns many fine rifles, goes to fight Mexicans armed with a shotgun, a pouch of beads, a knife, and a lance."

Geronimo stared moodily into the darkness. Since fleeing from the encampment he had lived only to go back to Kas-Kai-Ya. But much time had been needed to plan an expedition large enough to attack the *rurales* there.

New weapons had been fashioned. Countless messages had been exchanged by Mangus Coloradus, Cochise, and Whoa, the three chiefs. The women and children of all three tribes had been taken to mountain retreats whose only approaches consisted of narrow canyons that a few warriors might defend. Then those retreats had been stocked with ample provisions and fuel.

Planning the campaign had been no easy task. Every warrior burned to go into Mexico and fight the *rurales*. Nobody wanted to stay home to guard the women and children. Nor would any warrior serve under any leader except his own chief.

Finally each of the three leaders had chosen his picked men. Mangus Coloradus included among his warriors all who had been at Kas-

Kai-Ya. Now, with two hundred and fifty braves under Cochise, two hundred under Mangus Coloradus, and a hundred and fifty led by Whoa, they were well into Mexico.

Each of the three divisions kept apart from the others, but not so far apart that they would be unable to join forces when it was time for a battle. Naiche preferred to travel with the Mimbreno Apaches rather than with the Chiricahuas led by his father, Cochise. This was because of his great liking for Geronimo.

Geronimo said finally, "I took the beads from the Mexicans. Now I return them. That is only justice."

"Only justice," Naiche agreed. An owl hooted three times, and Naiche said, "The signal. A scout returns."

Geronimo said, "Come."

They rose and made their way to the camp of Mangus Coloradus. A short time later, dressed as a Mexican and driving a burro, Pedro Gonzalez loomed up in the darkness. He had been to Mexico in advance of the warriors to gather such information as he could.

Mangus Coloradus rose to meet him. "What saw you?" he asked.

"I saw *rurales*," Pedro said. "I even talked with them, since they thought me a Mexican. There are two companies of foot soldiers and two companies of horse soldiers. Among them are those who attacked us at Kas-Kai-Ya. But they are not now at Kas-Kai-Ya. They are at Arispe, in the Mexican state of Sonora and to the west of Kas-Kai-Ya."

Geronimo blurted, "Then we go to Arispe!"

"To Arispe!" Naiche echoed.

Mangus Coloradus asked haughtily, "Do warriors decide where the battle shall be fought?"

"I will fight the *rurales* who killed my wife, my mother, and my children," Geronimo said stubbornly. "If we must attack the people of Kas-Kai-Ya, that may come afterwards."

Naiche growled, "I fight beside my friend."

"We will all go to Arispe," Mangus Coloradus said. "We will start at once. For in truth we must fight the *rurales* who massacred our people."

"I shall tell Cochise," Naiche said.

Mangus Coloradus said, "Ask Cochise to inform Whoa. Tell both that we join forces before Arispe."

"I shall inform Whoa," Naiche promised.

Naiche disappeared in the darkness. The word spread like wind-driven wildfire, and warriors prepared to march. Nobody was mounted. Even with almost a year to make ready, there had not been enough time to capture war horses for everyone. Besides, so great a number of horsemen would be far easier to detect than foot soldiers, so nobody rode.

Geronimo felt in the darkness to make sure his knife was at his belt. In turn he fingered his powder horn, the pouch of beads, his parcel of jerked meat, and his parcel of parched corn.

He hung over his shoulder the blanket that served him as bed by night and clothing by day. Like all the rest of the warriors, he was going into battle wearing as little clothing as possible, and the blanket would be flung aside when the fight started. Taking his lance in his left hand, Geronimo carried his shotgun in his right hand.

Mangus Coloradus said, "Lead on."

Geronimo strode into the darkness. Partly because he knew Mexico so well, and partly because of his marvelous sense of direction, he had been appointed guide for the entire expedition.

In late afternoon of the third day following, they came before the walled town of Arispe.

They halted in a woods some five hundred yards from the town, and Geronimo's heart leaped as he stood beside Naiche. Again, in imagination, he saw his mother, his wife, his murdered children. A great joy rose within him at the knowledge that, only a short distance away, their murderers awaited. The Apaches had come upon Arispe so stealthily that the *rurales* couldn't possibly have fled. A battle was assured.

But their presence must be known soon,

and when they were discovered they could expect action from Arispe. The sun was sinking when Naiche said:

"They come."

Eight townsmen bearing a white flag of truce left the walled town and walked toward the trees. Geronimo could not help admiring them. Eight Mexicans who approached any number of Apaches *must* be courageous.

"What would you do with them, brother?" Naiche asked, stepping closer to Geronimo.

"Hold them prisoner and force the *rurales* to come out to attempt a rescue," replied Geronimo. "Thus we may be sure of a battle."

"Their flag says they come to talk. It is not honorable to capture them."

"The *rurales* who slew our women and children at Kas-Kai-Ya were less than honorable too," Geronimo said grimly.

"That is true, but whether we capture or parley is for the chiefs to say. Let us hear."

They made their way to where Mangus Coloradus, Cochise, and Whoa awaited the eight townsmen. No Apache stirred until the Mexicans were so near the woods that there was no possible chance of their running back into Arispe. Then Mangus Coloradus ordered:

"Capture them so the *rurales* must try a rescue."

Geronimo and Naiche remained with the chiefs, for they scorned to fight townsmen. But other warriors ran forward. The Mexicans halted and grouped together, each man with his back against a companion's.

Pedro Gonzalez, one of those attempting the capture, said in Spanish, "Submit and you will not be hurt."

"You come to kill!" a Mexican snarled, and eight hands flew to knives.

The encircling warriors drew their own knives. Near-naked Apaches ringed the Mexicans and it was over. Pedro Gonzalez came to the chiefs.

"We would have captured them, but they chose to fight," he said.

"It is no matter," Cochise shrugged. "The *rurales* will come now for revenge."

The next morning some of the soldier police did come. Twenty horsemen galloped toward the woods where the Apaches were hiding, fired wildly into them, and retreated without hurting anyone. That evening the Apaches captured a Mexican supply train whose leaders knew nothing of the powerful war party concealed near the town. Besides a store of food, the Apaches took many guns and much ammunition.

At ten o'clock the next morning, the *rurales* came in force. Two companies of infantry in battle formation advanced toward the woods where the Apaches were still hidden. Two of cavalry were held in reserve just outside the town walls.

Lying near the chiefs, with Naiche on one side and Nadeze on the other, Geronimo poured powder into the cavernous muzzle of his shotgun. He emptied the pouch of beads on top of it, tamped them in with cloth, and primed the gun. Naiche grinned, understanding at last.

Nadeze exclaimed, "There are the murderers of Kas-Kai-Ya!"

"So?" Mangus Coloradus said calmly. "What think you, Cochise? What think you, Whoa? These enemies slew Geronimo's mother. They slew his wife. They slew his children. Should Geronimo lead the first attack?"

"It is well," Cochise murmured.

"It is just," Whoa agreed.

Geronimo turned to Naiche. "Take fifty warriors and go unseen into that strip of woods we see from here. Wait until the enemies are past and we have attacked. Then charge them from the rear."

"I go, brother," Naiche said grimly. "Good hunting."

When the *rurales* were four hundred yards away they stopped to fire. Those in front kneeled so that those behind could shoot over their heads. Keeping his men hidden, Geronimo noticed that every weapon was discharged.

The *rurales* fired a second volley from two hundred yards and, as before, every weapon was emptied. Now, before they could reload, was the time to take them.

Shotgun in one hand, lance in the other, Geronimo sounded the Apache war whoop and raced out of the woods toward the enemy. The Mexicans worked desperately with their guns, but fewer than half reloaded in time. The remainder drew sabers and awaited the attack.

When only fifty feet separated Geronimo from the Mexicans, he leveled his shotgun, cocked it, and fired. The weapon spewed its glass beads forth, and half a dozen Mexicans fell. Flinging the now-useless shotgun from him, Geronimo leveled his lance and raced on.

He saw Naiche and his warriors swarm out of the woods to attack from the rear. At the same time he saw the Mexican cavalry charge to the aid of their hard-pressed comrades.

An officer, saber raised, rode straight at Geronimo, determined to ride him down. Geronimo sidestepped, thrust with his lance, brought the officer out of his saddle, and lost his lance in doing so.

Armed with only a knife, he awaited the next horseman. He dodged beneath the soldier's saber, caught the arm that wielded it, and pulled the *rurale* from his saddle. They rolled in a desperate struggle for the saber until a stray bullet, ricocheting across the battlefield, buried itself in the *rurale's* brain and he went limp.

Geronimo leaped to his feet, grabbed the saber, and went on fighting with it until he took another lance from a dead Apache.

Before sunset, the battered remnants of the *rurales* were trembling behind Arispe's walls. There would be wailing soon in some of the lodges of the Mimbreno, the Nedni, the Chiricahuas. But for every Mimbreno who had been slaughtered in the massacre of Kas-Kai-Ya, and for every warrior who had died before Arispe, two *rurales* lay dead on the field of battle.

CHAPTER SEVEN

The White Men

HIDDEN by brush, Geronimo lay motionless on a hilltop and riveted his eyes on the scene below.

He was watching a man, one of the strange white men whom Geronimo had first seen when surveyors came to mark the boundary between the United States and Mexico. The man was leading four burros, each with a pack on its back. He was approaching a bluff.

Hiding behind the bluff, Geronimo saw two other white men on horses. When the man with the burros was near enough, the two leaped their horses in front of him. Leveling pistols, they said something Geronimo could not hear but was obviously menacing.

The man dropped his burros' lead ropes and raised both hands. The horsemen dismounted. While one continued to point his pistol at the man with the burros, the other rummaged through the packs. Presently he turned to his companion and exclaimed:

"Gold!"

"So you made a strike, Pop?" the other man asked. "Where is it?"

" 'Twas just a pocket," the man with the burro quavered.

"Better not lie to us, Pop."

He who had searched the packs encircled the prospector's throat with one arm and held tight while the other man tied him. Then they built a fire and in it thrust a knife.

Grimacing, Geronimo stole down to where he had left his hunting horse. Apaches tortured prisoners, but only when they seemed to have important military information that they would not reveal. Even then, Geronimo had seen battle-hardened warriors turn away because they could not look upon the prisoner's suffering.

Mounting his horse, Geronimo heard the prospector shriek as his captors used the red-hot knife to make him tell where the gold mine was. He put his horse to a run because he cared to hear no more screams, and slowed only when he was out of hearing.

Not once did he even imagine that the prospector's body would be found by other white men and the killing would be considered as another terrible crime of Apaches.

After a while Geronimo stopped beneath another hill. He tethered his trained hunting horse. Bow in hand and arrow-filled quiver on his shoulder, he crawled up the hill so carefully that even a stalking cat would have been more noticeable.

Reaching the top, he looked down upon fifteen antelope. Very slowly, for antelope have wonderful eyes that notice the least move, he took two arrows from his quiver. One he nocked loosely in his bow, then laid

the bow where he could grasp it instantly. To the feathered end of the other arrow he tied a strip of cloth. He raised this second arrow so that the cloth appeared above the grass, and waved it slowly back and forth.

Every antelope swung at once to gaze at this

wonder. They turned their heads this way and that, stamped their hoofs, and blew through their nostrils. Then they let curiosity overcome caution and walked forward for a closer look.

When they were well within range, Geronimo dropped the arrow. In the same instant he seized and drew his bow and rose to one knee. The antelope whirled to run, but the hunting arrow Geronimo loosed caught a fat buck in mid-leap and brought him to earth dead. Geronimo dressed his game, tied it behind the hunting horse's saddle, and rode on to meet Naiche. He found his friend, who also had a fat antelope, waiting near the rocky spire where they had agreed to meet.

"I saw a great herd of antelope," Naiche announced. "I might have killed several, but I need only one."

Geronimo said, "I found only a small herd of antelope, but I saw three white men. I could not attack because they have guns and I carry only a bow and arrows. Two of the white men tied the third and burned him with a hot knife blade."

"All white men are crazy," Naiche growled. "And there are far too many of them in land that belongs to Apaches."

[74]

THE WHITE MEN

"There are not as many as there were," Geronimo pointed out. "It has come to my ears that they could not find enough Indians to kill, so they started a great fight among themselves. I have heard they call it the Civil War, and all the soldiers who were in Apache country have gone to kill each other."

Naiche said, "Let us wish them great success in such a worthy undertaking. Now is the time for Apaches to kill the white men who remain and again be masters in our own land."

"We are fast becoming masters," Geronimo said. "The three men I saw today must be either great fools or of great courage. Most white men dare not leave their cities of Tucson and Tubac unless they are in numbers and well armed. Their stages no longer run, and their mail carriers no longer ride. The ashes of their wagons are blowing throughout Apache land. Their houses and stage stations are abandoned to the sun and wind. Their graves are more than one man may count."

"True," Naiche agreed. "But I worry."

"For what reason?"

Naiche spoke thoughtfully. "First came the men who measured land and drove stakes in the ground. They left and we Apaches rested easier. Then came rock scratchers, gold seekers, to Pinos Altos, and again we had cause for anxiety.

"Thinking to be rid of the rock scratchers, Mangus Coloradus himself went among them and offered to lead them south to rich gold mines in the Sierra Madre. Truly the gold was there. And truly Mangus Coloradus would have led them to it, for at that time we had not yet learned the worth of gold. But the miners thought your Mimbreno chief was lying. They overpowered and bound him. Then they flogged him more mercilessly than we ever flogged the most rebellious Mexican prisoner.

"I worry because Mangus Coloradus is

growing old," Naiche went on. "He cannot forget that white men fought us with weapons better than our own. When we won or stole such weapons for ourselves, they came with still better ones. Mangus Coloradus thinks that, when the white men are weary of killing each other, they will return with weapons even more terrible. He thinks the only hope for Apaches is to seek peace. Yet he fights on."

Geronimo said, "The only hope is to fight for that which is ours."

"I agree, but I worry for another reason," Naiche said. "My father, Cochise, long kept the peace. He let the white men run their stages. He protected their wagons and mail carriers from renegades who would have destroyed them.

"Then, only a few moons ago, a white chief named Bascom came to Apache Pass with some soldiers. He summoned Cochise to his tent, saying he wanted to talk. Suspecting no treachery, Cochise went with five warriors. Bascom said we Chiricahuas had stolen a boy named Mickey Free and some cattle. He demanded their return."

Geronimo said, "I have not heard all this story."

"Cochise denied that Chiricahuas had stolen either the boy or the cattle," Naiche

went on. "Bascom gave him the lie and ordered his soldiers to make prisoners of those
who had come to talk. Cochise escaped by
slashing the tent with his knife and running.
But the warriors were captured. So we captured some white men."

There was a moody silence while Naiche
pondered his words. He continued:

"Meanwhile a white chief named Irwin,
who outranked Bascom, came to Apache Pass.
We sent word to him that we would free our
white captives if our warriors were freed. Instead, while we watched from surrounding
cliffs, Irwin had them killed in the peculiar
fashion of white men. He tied ropes around
their necks and let them dangle from a tree
until they were dead. In turn, we killed our
white prisoners."

"I was raiding in Mexico at the time, for I
have raided Mexicans at every opportunity
since the massacre at Kas-Kai-Ya," Geronimo
said. "I wish that I had been present."

Naiche said, "If you had been, you would
have seen for yourself why the Chiricahuas
are at war with the white men. But, though
no warrior is more courageous nor any chief
more wise, I know my father. He wars with
them now, but in his heart he, too, thinks

that we must some day make peace with the white men."

"There is no peace at present," Geronimo said, "so let us return to the village, get guns, and kill the two white men I have just seen. We shall not find the third alive."

"Let us do that," Naiche agreed.

They rode into the Chiricahua encampment just in time to see the women and children, with an escort of warriors, leaving. The remaining warriors were looking to their weapons. Naiche and Geronimo made their way to Cochise, who was calmly giving orders to sub-chiefs.

"Why should this be?" Naiche inquired.

"Our scouts bring word that many soldiers from the land to the west, who call themselves the California Volunteers, are marching in this direction. They go to fight in the war that other white men are fighting to the east," Cochise said. "The path they have chosen will lead them through Apache Pass. I have sent word to Mangus Coloradus to join us. Then we will kill every soldier!"

At the exciting news of a great battle in store, Geronimo and Naiche forgot all about the two white men whom they had intended to find and kill.

CHAPTER EIGHT

The Battle of Apache Pass

HIGH on the steep and boulder-strewn side of narrow Apache Pass, Geronimo lay behind a pile of rocks. He had made the little breastwork appear natural by uprooting a cactus and standing it on top of the rocks. His best rifle and all the powder and bullets he had been able to gather lay within easy reach. Now he had only to await the soldiers, who intended to march through Apache Pass, and to give thanks to Usan, who had created an ambush so perfect.

Apache Pass was a narrow slit between the Chiricahua Mountains on the west and the Dos Cabezas on the east. It was one of the very few passes in the Southwest through which travelers could take wagons. Far more important, in a land of little water it sheltered sweet and cool springs that never failed.

Turning his head, Geronimo saw the stone house built by men of the Overland Stage Company and abandoned since Cochise took the warpath. Some six hundred yards beyond the house, tall trees and green grass marked the flowing springs.

Geronimo smacked his lips in satisfaction.

Behind each rock in the pass, each shrub, each cluster of cactus, crouched an armed Apache. There were almost seven hundred Mimbrenos and Chiricahuas. They were so well hidden that even Geronimo, who knew they were there, could see few of them. He smacked his lips again.

The scouts had reported that there were about as many white soldiers as there were Apaches in ambush, some on foot and some mounted. The soldiers had stopped with their supply train at Dragoon Springs, forty miles west of Apache Pass. There they could drink to their heart's content, water their stock, and load up with enough water to see them through to Apache Pass. But their water would be gone by the time they entered the pass, and they could not get more until they reached the springs beyond the stone stage-house.

Geronimo glanced with pleasure at the

stone breastworks which Mangus Coloradus and Cochise had had built on the heights overlooking these springs. The fortifications were manned by warriors who could shoot without being shot, since the breastworks protected them.

Unable to renew their water supplies, the soldiers who were not killed by bullets would die from thirst. The greatest Apache victory of all time was almost certain.

Soon two Apache scouts who had gone out to watch for the soldiers' arrival came into

the pass. One went to Cochise's ambush. The second turned to where Mangus Coloradus lay.

Geronimo burned to know what the scouts had seen and what they were saying, for then he would know how soon he might expect battle. But he did not leave his position.

Presently, Naiche slipped down beside Geronimo. He was grinning.

"Most of the heavy wagons, without which white soldiers go nowhere, remain at Dragoon Springs," he said. "A few horse and many foot soldiers are coming to Apache Pass, but they are no more than one to our six. They wear their foolish uniforms of blue cloth and they reel with the heat. They cannot live without water."

"Nor can they get water," Geronimo's grin reflected Naiche's. "Before they reach it we shall slay them all."

"We shall slay them all," Naiche agreed.

Naiche slipped back to his ambush. A half hour later Geronimo saw the thin cloud of dust that hovered above the marching soldiers.

The soldiers entered Apache Pass, and most of the cavalrymen led their mounts, for the horses were so desperate for water that they could not be ridden. There were pack animals too, and they carried strange wheels and tubes that were typical of the silly things white soldiers took into battle. But in spite of heat, thirst, and the heavy uniforms, the white men kept a smart military formation as they walked unsuspectingly into the trap.

They were two thirds of the way into the pass when a shot from the rifle of Cochise rang out. At once firearms blazed from behind the Indians' breastworks. But the hoped-for massacre did not come about.

This was partly because the Apaches were so sure the soldiers could not escape that they did not bother aiming as carefully as they should have. And it was partly because so many of the Indians were shooting smooth-bore muskets that were not accurate at a long distance.

Even as he shot at them, Geronimo could not help admiring soldiers such as these white men. They did not flee in panic, as Mexicans nearly always did, but coolly shot back. In good order, shooting as they went and taking their wounded with them, they retreated from the pass.

Geronimo swallowed his disappointment. He had hoped all the soldiers might be slaughtered at the first volley. But he knew that those who still lived must reach the springs or die of thirst.

Leaving his position, Geronimo raced to the heights overlooking the springs. He found a place behind the breastworks on the heights and waited.

The white soldiers came again. But they were in battle formation this time, and their rifles were far superior to smoothbores. Every shot from an ambushed Indian drew a quick reply. Soldiers dropped, but here and there an Apache went limp too. Carrying their dead and such wounded as could not help themselves, the soldiers fought their way to the stone stagehouse. Some entered the building, and some sheltered themselves behind it.

Geronimo made ready for the attack on those who would attempt to get to the springs. He had thought not even one soldier would ever reach the stagehouse, but most were there. However, they were still six hundred yards from the water they must have and the deadliest ambush of all.

The soldiers stayed in or behind the stagehouse for almost an hour and a half. When they came out and advanced toward the springs, Geronimo was amazed to see them pulling little wagons with tubes mounted on them. Only warriors who knew nothing of battle would bother with such clumsy things. Geronimo's confidence rose.

The soldiers neared the springs, and the Apaches loosed a rain of bullets. Again, very few soldiers were hit.

It seemed to the puzzled Geronimo that the others were very busy with their little wagons.

The first shell struck the breastworks

One wagon escaped from the men who were handling it and started to roll. Immediately other men pounced upon and halted it. They turned the little wagon about, so that the tube pointed at the breastworks.

The first shell—for the little wagons were really howitzers—struck the breastworks squarely about thirty feet to one side of Geronimo. Dust, dirt, stones, boulders, and Apaches flew into the air.

The rest of the Apaches waited in stunned silence until the second shell exploded. Then the Indians began a panicky scramble up the slope.

When they reached the heights, Geronimo stood with Mangus Coloradus and twenty other Mimbreno braves and looked down on the battle ground. They watched the soldiers drink, fill canteens, and retreat with their horses to the stone stagehouse.

"We would have killed them all, but they shot wagons at us," Mangus Coloradus said wonderingly. "But we are still many more than they are, and we will kill them yet. To do so, we must first kill the messengers they will surely send for help. Come."

The warriors followed Mangus Coloradus to the west end of the pass. Soon they heard the pounding of horses' hoofs. A moment later they saw the five mounted messengers who were riding to warn those camped at Dragoon Springs of the ambush and to ask for help.

The Indians shot. Three horses went down at the first volley, but two riders were quickly pulled up behind two other soldiers and thundered on. There remained no one to help the rider of the third downed horse.

In the thickening night, the Apaches advanced to kill this lone man. The dismounted trooper crouched behind his dead horse and prepared to sell his life as dearly as possible.

The trooper's carbine cracked. Geronimo and two other warriors caught Mangus Coloradus as he fell and carried him behind an outjutting shoulder of rock.

They forgot all about the trooper who, after the Apaches left, made his way to his companions at the stagehouse and lived to tell the tale.

CHAPTER NINE

A Wounded Chief

THE sorrowful warriors gathered around
their wounded chief. Grieving because he
was hurt, they were also worried. While Mangus Coloradus led them, even though they
might suffer temporary defeats, in the end
they always triumphed. What now?

Nadeze said, "We need a medicine man."

"I am a medicine man," Geronimo said.

Geronimo told the truth. Following the
massacre of Kas-Kai-Ya, he had taken the
training which he needed in order to become
an Apache medicine man. This he had done
in the hope that he might discover some powerful medicine which would make sure the
defeat of the *rurales* responsible for the massacre. But even though he had learned all the
rituals that an Apache medicine man must
know, he was far too intelligent to have much

faith in them. But others believed in them. He said again, "I am a medicine man." "True," Nadeze agreed. "I had forgotten." Opening his pouch of *hoddentin,* or sacred pollen, Geronimo rubbed a bit on Mangus Coloradus' forehead. Then he made a cross of *hoddentin* on the chief's breast. He sprinkled a thin line of the sacred pollen all around

the Mimbreno leader and put a touch on the forehead of every warrior who stood near. Finally, he applied a pinch to his own forehead and took a bit in his mouth.

And even as he finished, he knew that *hoddentin* was not enough.

Geronimo was not so blinded by the ways

of the Apaches that he was unable to see for himself that other people had better ways. Often he had seen *rurales* so badly wounded that he thought they could never fight again. Yet, in a later skirmish, he had fought the same *rurales,* and apparently they were as whole as before.

With the rest of the nearby Mimbreno braves too stricken to do anything, and no sub-chief near, Geronimo took charge.

He said, "Make a litter."

"Where do we go with my father?" asked Mangas, son of Mangus Coloradus.

"To the Mexican medicine man at Janos," Geronimo said.

Mangas said, "The Mexicans are enemies."

"That I know," Geronimo grunted.

He paid no more attention to Mangas. Though a brave warrior, the son of Mangus Coloradus lacked the qualities that made his father great. When he was forced to make an important decision, Mangas was never able to decide on the wise course and always trembled between the two.

Geronimo was not a chief, but the other warriors obeyed him now because he acted like one. Some went to fashion a litter of deer skins or deer-skin jackets stretched between

cottonwood poles. Some went to rally the rest
of the Mimbreno warriors. As word reached
the followers of Mangus Coloradus they gathered around their stricken chief.

Mangas said, "If all of us depart, the Chiricahuas alone must battle the white soldiers."

"Let them," Geronimo grunted sourly.

He could not know that the Chiricahuas
were to fight again, and to be defeated again,
the next day. Had the Mimbrenos stayed to
help, the soldiers might have been defeated.
Then, at least until the Civil War ended and
more soldiers came, the combined Apache
forces probably would have retaken all their
homeland.

But almost none of the Mimbreno warriors
had any thought for anything save the badly
wounded Mangus Coloradus. Under his lead-
ership, they had become a very powerful
tribe. If they were robbed of his wisdom, who
knew what might happen?

Stockily built Victorio, a cold-eyed, fero-
cious Mimbreno sub-chief, had hurried to
Mangus Coloradus as soon as he heard of his
wound. Now he said:

"I will help carry our leader. Guide us,
Geronimo."

He picked up one end of the litter. Mangas took the other. Geronimo led the way through the darkness. He dropped pinches of *hoddentin* as he walked, for this was supposed to make the wounded Mangus Coloradus' path much easier. But the seventy-year-old chief was unable to speak above a whisper during the long and difficult journey.

Stopping only to hunt food and for snatches of sleep, the Mimbrenos carried him over mountains and across deserts. At last they were in Mexico, before the gates of the walled town of Janos.

The *rurales* of the town came out to meet them. Though they were armed and in considerable force, the *rurales* were afraid. The Mimbreno braves were in full strength. They also were fully armed, and with no women and children to hamper them.

Murmuring prayers, the *rurales* made ready to defend themselves and the townspeople. But Geronimo stepped up to their captain.

"We come in peace," he said. "Our chief is wounded, and we bring him to your medicine man."

A sweat of fear bathed the captain's face, but a gasp of relief escaped his lips. There was hope. This was no war party.

The captain dismounted, gave his horse's

The Mimbrenos carried him over mountains
and across deserts

reins to a private, and walked beside Geronimo and the two men carrying Mangus Coloradus' litter. Men, women, and children shrank against houses or scurried away as the procession made its way to the doctor's house.

"They come in peace. Their chief is wounded and they wish only to bring him to our doctor," the captain explained to whoever remained near enough to hear.

Those who heard passed the word to others. Then all the people of Janos hurried to the church. Often they had wished that Mangus Coloradus might die. Now they prayed for his life, for they feared that, if he died, the angered Apaches would kill everybody in Janos.

When they reached the doctor's house, Mangas and Victorio carried Mangus Coloradus in. Most of the warriors took up positions outside the house so that no one might come near. The captain of the *rurales* and Geronimo entered with the litter bearers.

Geronimo addressed the doctor.

"Make him well."

The doctor was a slender man, not young enough so that his hair was all dark but not old enough so that it was all white. The hard life he had led in Janos had taught him to fear nothing. Stepping close to the litter, he looked at the wounded chief.

"Put him on the table," he said.

Mangas and Victorio lifted Mangus Coloradus to a rude wooden table and stepped back against the wall. Geronimo watched Mangus Coloradus steadily.

There had been times during the long march when the Mimbreno chief's wound had caused him to sleep, and times when his mind had wandered. But he was awake now and he knew what was taking place. He was ready to meet this as he had always met everything else. Whatever came, his eyes would be toward it, and his heart would be strong.

Though outwardly the Apaches showed nothing of what they thought or felt, inwardly they were taut as stretched buckskin. The captain of the *rurales,* hoping Mangus Coloradus would live and fearing the consequences if he died, was staring, gasping, and sweating. The doctor and the Mimbreno chief were the only calm people in the room.

The doctor examined the wound, shook his head doubtfully, and the captain of the *rurales* cried aloud. The doctor looked sternly at him and said:

"Captain Ruiz, if you cannot control yourself, be good enough to leave."

"I'll stay, and I'll be quiet," Captain Ruiz promised.

With a delicate, but firm and sure touch, the doctor slipped a probe into the bullet wound. Mangus Coloradus did not cry out, but pain brought a bath of sweat to his forehead.

Mangas stepped angrily forward. Geronimo reached out a hand to stop him. The doctor again shook his head doubtfully, and Captain Ruiz clapped a hand over his mouth to stifle another cry.

Again the probe went in, gently but surely.

Two hours after the chief had been laid on the table, the doctor took the bullet from Mangus Coloradus. He applied a compress of soothing herbs and held them in place with a bandage. Then he turned to Geronimo, Victorio, Mangas, and Captain Ruiz.

"He'll live," he said.

Thus the Mimbreno Apaches came to Janos and left without harming a single person.

CHAPTER TEN

A Chief Dies

SITTING on a hillock beside Victorio, Geronimo's restless eyes sought the valley beneath, the next hill, and the hills beyond. Often he turned his head to look behind him. The years had taught Geronimo that an enemy might come from anywhere at any time. He who failed to see the enemy first was apt to die swiftly.

Victorio's eyes searched the hills, too, despite a frown that told of a troubled mind.

"It is possible," he said as he continued his conversation with Geronimo, "that the Mangus Coloradus who was, leaked out through the white soldier's bullet hole. We did not bring the same chief from Janos that we took to the medicine man."

"I have often wondered if the Mexican

doctor did not put a spell upon him," Geronimo remarked. "Many times I have thought of going back to Janos and killing him. But I have thought each time that even Mangus Coloradus could not suffer such a wound without being ill. It is a natural thing."

"A natural thing," Victorio agreed, "and for many days he was ill. Remember the snail-pace we were forced to keep when we finally left Janos? It is a good thing we were many, for even Mexicans might have overtaken us. But Mangus Coloradus is ill no longer. Still he counsels that Apaches must make peace with white men or there will be no more Apaches."

Geronimo said, "He lives much in the spirit world. I entered his wickiup to speak to him, and he said, 'I am happy to see you once more, Delgadito. Now you must tell our people that we cannot conquer these Americans as we did the Mexicans.' Ha! Delgadito died many years ago in a battle with Mexicans. Yet Mangus Coloradus talked with him when he should have been talking with me. It chilled me, for I cannot talk with spirits."

"Nor can I," said Victorio. "I can talk only with people and be guided only by them and by my own common sense. Good sense tells me that if we do not fight the Americans, they will overrun us and there will be no more Apaches anyway. In spite of the fact that they still war among themselves, they have soldiers to spare for Apache land. White men who come among us are more instead of fewer, but only the Chiricahuas still fight them."

"Mangus Coloradus points that out," Geronimo said. "The warriors of Cochise kill and are killed by soldiers, cattle drivers, and rock scratchers who are forever looking for gold. But it is as though every dead white man is a seed from which two more spring up."

"Do you think that?" Victorio questioned.

"There is reason for so thinking," Geronimo said. "But I also think we must fight until every white man is driven from our land or until all Apaches are killed. If white men become our masters we shall know sorry times indeed. Do you know they call us thieves, liars, murderers, and every other vile name their tongues can form? Ha! Any Apache can take lessons in thievery, lying, and murder from any white man!"

"What do you mean?" Asked Victorio.

Geronimo said, "When the white men

warred against Mexico, Apaches sold them horses and mules and brought them food. We told them to take the places called Sonora and Chihuahua and we would help. They accepted our help when it was needed. The war ended and for a time no more was heard.

"Then came a surveyor named Bartlett, and he sent word that he was a good friend to all Apaches. We believed and trusted him, but when we brought our Mexican slaves to his camp, Bartlett took them away.

"It seems that, when the war ended, Americans and Mexicans became brothers. Bartlett said it was wrong to make slaves of his brothers. He said also that the Americans' God frowns upon those who keep slaves. Ha! I have since learned that the Americans keep millions of slaves themselves!"

"It was a great lie," Victorio said.

"A very great lie," Geronimo agreed, "but far from the greatest. Bartlett's real purpose in coming here was to mark where this land ends and Mexico begins. The Americans were at war with Mexico. They might have taken the whole country by force of arms, but when they wanted land, they bought and paid for it.

"That was very silly, and it was just as silly for the Americans to think they bought land from Mexico that Mexico never owned. They paid Mexico for .our land, the country of the Apaches. Then they told us, 'We bought you when we bought your land. Obey our laws, or we shall punish you.' Was there ever a greater swindle?"

"Never!" Victorio growled.

"So we fight white men whom we would never hurt at all, if they just stayed home. And they call us evil! Suppose we went to the people of the north, the Canadians, and paid money for the lands of the Americans. Then suppose we told the Americans that they must live by Apache laws or be punished. Would they not resist?"

"Fiercely," Victorio growled. "I agree with you that we must fight, but the Mimbreno warriors follow Mangus Coloradus and will for as long as he is chief. Let us go see if we might again persuade him to be a war chief and lead us against the white men."

The two made their way to the Mimbreno village, and knew as soon as they looked upon it that something unusual was taking place. People scurried here and there, dogs barked, and horses on a nearby hill were nervous.

Victorio and Geronimo began to run. They saw Mangus Coloradus in the center of the village surrounded by a group of his people. Beside him was a bearded white man whom Geronimo recognized as Jack Swilling, a skilled frontiersman who had lived for a long time in the Southwest. Towering over everyone in the group, old Mangus Coloradus was as erect at seventy-two as he had been at seventeen. His hair was snow-white now. But it was still abundant, and it had just been carefully dressed. He wore his finest moccasins and buckskins, and he was talking calmly.

"Long have I led the Mimbreno Apaches, and always my first thoughts have been for my people. Of late I have been greatly troubled. Constant war is a poor companion, and starvation is a thankless bedfellow.

"Now comes this messenger from Captain Shirland, of the United States Army. He asks us to go into Captain Shirland's camp bearing a white flag, and he brings Captain Shirland's own pledged word that neither I nor any who choose to go with me shall suffer harm. He has promised that the Mimbreno Apaches will have their own reservation and plenty of food. I believe, and I would lead all who choose to go with me to peace and plenty."

Geronimo flung himself forward and knelt before his chief. "Think!" he pleaded.

"Think carefully before you do this thing!
The white men will have much cause for boast-
ing if they may say that Mangus Coloradus is
their prisoner!"

"It is a trick!" Victorio warned.

Mangus Coloradus spoke with the dignity
of a chief and from the wisdom of years.
"You, Geronimo, and you, Victorio, have
ever been two of the most hot-headed warriors. Nothing I can say will make you believe
that you cannot continue to battle the white

man. Experience alone must teach you. Rise and let me pass."

Geronimo rose to his feet and soon Mangus Coloradus and the little group who had chosen to go with him left the village.

The evening fires had been lighted six times and were lighted again when Diablo, a young warrior who had gone with Mangus Coloradus, shuffled back into the village. His eyes were downcast, his tread weary. He walked slowly to a fire and stared at it. For a long while he did not speak.

"You saw?" Geronimo questioned.

"I saw," Diablo said dully.

"What saw you?"

Diablo said, "We walked into the soldiers' camp. Mangus Coloradus carried the white flag that should have been our protection, but soldiers rose up and seized him. They tied our chief as we might tie a Mexican, or a dog. The rest of us they herded into an unused stable. I know the rest of the story from Acona, an Apache scout who is serving the soldiers."

Diablo quieted and stared intently into the fire, as though he could not go on. At last he continued.

"Into the camp came a Colonel West, an

Army chief who outranks Captain Shirland. He talked with some of the soldiers. The soldiers loosed Mangus Coloradus' bonds and left. Only two soldiers remained on guard.

"Our chief, old and ill, and who must have been weary, lay down by the fire. He slept. One of the guards thrust the long knife, the bayonet that white soldiers carry on the end of their guns, into the fire. When the bayonet glowed red with heat, the soldier touched it against our chief. Mangus Coloradus sprang up, as who would not? He started to run, as who would not if awakened in such a fashion? There were two shots and . . ."

Diablo fell silent and stared moodily into the fire.

CHAPTER ELEVEN

Geronimo in Chains

IN THE Apache camp at Warm Springs, New Mexico, Victorio and Geronimo braced themselves against the side of a big wooden building which had once been a barracks for white soldiers. All about them wickiups sprouted like misshapen plants. A large herd of horses grazed near by. Women and older children ground corn in their stone grinding bowls.

Others prepared freshly killed meat, but they were not working over the carcasses of elk, deer, and antelope. These were stolen range cattle that the women made ready for cooking pots. But they were as tasty as any wild game. And they also furnished a great deal more meat for every shot expended.

The warm sun had made Geronimo and

Victorio sleepy, so that neither warrior felt like moving unnecessarily. But their conversation was lively enough.

"The days of our fathers are truly gone, and I do not believe they will ever be again," said Geronimo. "Even war as we once knew it is no more. There was a time when Apaches fought more for adventure and plunder than anything else. But now, since the white men have become our enemies, both sides fight only to kill."

"That is how Cochise fought the white men for ten long years," Victorio remarked.

Geronimo said bitterly, "But finally even he made terms. He promised to fight no more if his Chiricahuas were permitted to stay in their homeland, the Chiricahua Mountains. General Howard, with whom Cochise treated, pledged his word that they might.

"Yet, less than eighteen months after Cochise has gone to join his ancestors, all his people have been rounded up by troops and shipped to a new reservation. It is somewhere here in New Mexico, and the Chiricahuas do not like it. Many have already deserted to go back on the warpath. Many more will desert. There will be much trouble."

Victorio said bitterly, "The white soldiers

are great fools. If they had left the Chiricahuas alone, there would have been no trouble. But has there ever been a time when white soldiers did not promise us one thing and give us another?"

"Why do you think I followed you to this place where you and your people have fled?" Geronimo queried. "I will not live with the other Apaches in that stinking country called the San Carlos Reservation which the white men saw fit to give them. And there are too many soldiers being stationed in Arizona. I knew that I and those few who came with me could not hope to fight them. It is good here."

"It is good here," Victorio agreed. "But only because the white soldiers are so stupid.

In Arizona, every group of soldiers starting on an Apache trail had many mules to carry provisions. Thus they were able to stay on the trail for many days or even weeks. Here in New Mexico, each soldier has only his own horse. When they set out to pursue us, they may continue only until their horses are too weary to go on. Then the soldiers must turn back."

"There is small need to fret about them," Geronimo said confidently. "For many years we have run away from all the soldiers in Arizona and New Mexico too. They will not catch us now."

Victorio said, "It is not the soldiers who worry me, but a white man who is now in

charge of the San Carlos Reservation. His name is John Clum, and he is no more like the ordinary white man who comes to oversee Indians than a jack rabbit is like an elk. He has treated the Apaches fairly, and as a result they have grown to respect him. Some of the bravest and best Apache warriors have joined his Indian police force. And he has vowed to put you and me, whom he calls renegades, on the reservation too."

"Let him talk," muttered Geronimo. "One cannot catch us with words."

He did not know that even as he spoke, John Clum and a number of his most fearless and sharpest-shooting Indian police were on their way to the camp. They had left San Carlos a week earlier for the sole purpose of capturing these two men and their followers.

For more than a year the Apaches had remained unmolested in this isolated camp in New Mexico. When they went to bed that night, they scarcely bothered to post a sentry.

In the first light of early morning John Clum and his Indian police closed in. Taken wholly by surprise, the Apaches could do nothing but surrender.

Geronimo felt the cold of iron manacles as they were clamped over his wrists. He and seven other troublemakers were chained together. John Clum directed a company of his police to take Victorio and his band to the Ojo Caliente reservation in Texas. All the rest were returned to San Carlos in Arizona.

Geronimo knew perfectly well that this reservation, along the banks of the Gila River, had been given to the Apaches only because no white man thought he would ever want the land. The reservation was blistering hot in summer and wind-blasted in winter. There was so little year-round rainfall that nothing would grow well except cactus, palo verde trees, greasewood, mesquite, and other desert vegetation.

Even as he arrived on the reservation, Geronimo knew that he would never stay. But all his ammunition and his rifle had been taken away. His knife was gone too. Since no warrior could travel far without weapons, Geronimo could do nothing for a while except bide his time and draw his rations of worm-ridden flour and tough, stringy beef.

But he was not idle, as he waited for a chance to escape. Searching daily, he found a bullet here, another there, and finally stole a rifle and hid it out on the desert. The agent who replaced John Clum was not interested in watching him closely. So Geronimo was able also to rebuild his horse herds through night raids on the Papagoes.

Other discontented Apaches were doing likewise.

One dark night, little more than a year after Geronimo had been brought to San Carlos in chains, a visitor came to his wickiup. He was Carlos Anaya, who had been one of Victorio's warriors.

"I come from the warpath," Carlos said softly to Geronimo.

"Victorio broke out?" Geronimo asked.

"Aye," Carlos said. "He left Ojo Caliente and fled south to join Caballero, chief of the Mescalero Apaches. Their combined forces made war throughout Texas, New Mexico, Arizona, and Old Mexico. They killed more than a thousand people.

"They forced many soldiers and many men called the Texas Rangers, and a vast number of the *rurales*, into the field against them. But finally most of them were killed. Only a few of us escaped. Still a warrior's death is better than a reservation life."

"Far better," said Geronimo. "I and those who follow me are almost ready to make a break for freedom too."

CHAPTER TWELVE

Flight into Mexico

THE lowering sun scorched Camp Good-win, the United States Army fort on the San Carlos reservation. But despite the sun, Geronimo had been sitting near the fort all day, as he had sat for the past six days, with a Navajo blanket draped about him and his fastest pony near at hand. He wanted the Indian agent at Camp Goodwin, a man named Hoag, to become accustomed to his sitting thus so that Hoag would pay no attention to him.

On this seventh day, plans that had been more than a year in the making were at last as perfect as they ever would be. Swift action lay ahead.

Geronimo's blanket hid a Winchester repeating rifle and bullet-filled belts. He watched a little group of Apaches, all mounted, riding southward. Nobody else paid any attention; the group might have been going hunting or wood gathering.

Geronimo returned his attention to Camp Goodwin. Two Apache chiefs named Loco and Nana, with most of their people, were gathered near the building. They all knew that Geronimo and another leader, Whoa, were about to make a break for Mexico with sixty warriors and a hundred and sixty women and children. Loco and Nana wanted to be sure that the agent could see them near the fort and know that they were taking no part in this break.

Geronimo wanted to make sure that neither chief told Hoag of the forthcoming flight. If there was any sign that they intended to betray his plans for escape, Geronimo would shoot them, and Loco and Nana both knew it.

Planning the flight had not been easy. And when the plans were made it had been necessary to choose the right time for the break. There would never be a better one than this afternoon. Many of the soldiers usually stationed at Camp Goodwin were away. Some were campaigning in New Mexico. Some were hunting outlaw Apaches who had been reported near the Arizona-Mexico border. Whoa had left early this morning to wait in a dry wash some miles to the south. All day long Apaches had been quietly drifting out to join him. They intended to start just before dark so they would have all night before the soldiers still in Camp Goodwin could take their trail.

Geronimo's eyes narrowed. Loco and Nana and their followers had done nothing. But the man named Sterling, Chief of San Carlos Police, now rode up with some Apache policemen. Had someone betrayed the careful plans? Or had Sterling intended to bring his Apache Police to Camp Goodwin anyhow?

The sun told Geronimo that it was a little past four o'clock. He rose. Still keeping the rifle hidden under his blanket, he walked to his pony and was preparing to mount when the man named Sterling shouted:

"Hey you! Wait!"

Pretending he did not know that he was being addressed, Geronimo did not look around. Sterling shouted again:

"I mean you, Geronimo! Stop or I'll shoot!"

Geronimo sprang to the saddle, dropping his blanket as he did so. Sterling's rifle cracked and a bullet sang close. Leveling his own rifle from the back of the already running pony, Geronimo flung a shot at Sterling. He bent low on his pony's back to make a smaller target as bullets from Sterling's Apache police whistled past. Then he galloped over a hill and was hidden.

Geronimo raced into the dry wash where the rest awaited him. All the warriors were on foot and holding their horses. The women and children were mounted, and some of the women held tightly to babies not yet old enough to ride alone. Most children, often with three on the same pony, managed their own mounts. Whoa, an Indian so big that he dwarfed the wiry little pony he rode, came to meet Geronimo.

"What news do you bring?" Whoa asked.

Geronimo said, "The man named Sterling came with his Apache police. He shot at me, and I shot at him, but I do not know if I hit him. The soldiers must know soon that we are gone."

"Come."

The warriors mounted. With an advance and rear guard, and scouts on either side, men, women, and children rode on at a fast trot.

Night fell, and they were safe until the sun rose again. But sunrise might find soldiers hot on their trail, so there could be no thought of sparing horses. The only sleep they dared allow themselves was such snatches as might be had in the saddle. From time to time they nibbled a bit of the parched corn or jerky, sun-dried beef that they carried in pouches.

With daylight, Geronimo reined in on top of a hill and looked behind him. There were no soldiers in sight and no cloud of dust, to indicate that any were coming. Geronimo turned and overtook Whoa.

"Nobody comes from the rear," he said,

"but we shall be in trouble soon. Our mounts reel from weariness."

"Yes," Whoa grunted.

Neither said more. Both had known that they and their people must travel fast. And both had also known that their horses and ponies could not run all the way to Mexico. They did not know yet what they would do when the animals were played out.

Some Apaches were asleep in the saddle, and now the fastest must suit their gait to the slowest. A pony stumbled, almost went down, then found his balance and pounded on. Suddenly Geronimo pointed ahead and exclaimed:

"Look! Usan has smiled upon us!"

A long pack train, with some horses and mules bearing packs and many more running loose, was making its way up the valley. Knowing how to get the last burst of speed from his tired pony, Geronimo whooped and sped to the attack. He began to shoot as soon as he was in range, and he heard the rifles of the rest of the warriors blasting behind him.

The white men and the Mexicans with them were outnumbered six to one. They fired a few hasty return shots and spurred

"Look! Usan has smiled upon us!"

out of danger, leaving their pack train and loose horses behind them. Letting the fleeing men go, Geronimo rode in ahead of the frightened horses and turned them. The warriors surrounded the herd.

There was a quick exchange of saddles and bridles, a swift rummaging through all the packs for priceless rifles and bullets, and most of the Apaches rode on.

Freshly mounted, Geronimo returned to the top of a hill for another look at the back trail. He could still see neither soldiers nor the telltale dust cloud to indicate any were coming. Geronimo hurried to catch Whoa.

"No soldiers are near enough to cause trouble from the rear," he reported. "So rather than go on at full speed, it would be wise to ride these fresh horses at a pace they can maintain."

"Wise indeed," Whoa said. "But let us not forget that some soldiers are elsewhere and even now may be returning to Camp Goodwin. We must be alert for whoever approaches from the front."

Geronimo said, "You speak wisely."

Alternately walking and trotting their mounts, they rode steadily toward Mexico. That day they stopped only long enough to let the thirsty Apache horses drink from a water hole. A herd of range horses was already drinking there, and they took those horses with them when they went on.

Into the night they traveled, and stopped again for two hours at another water hole. The horses drank and grazed. Some of the weariest people slept. Geronimo, who often had been afield a full week with only such sleep as he could get in the saddle, climbed a hill to look for danger on the back trail.

The next day, riding as advance scout, Geronimo saw soldiers coming a moment before they saw him. There were two companies, about sixty men, of the Fourth Cavalry, and they were directly in the path the Apaches must follow. Geronimo waved his rifle as a signal that enemies were sighted, and the warriors whooped to join him.

This was Apache country, a land in which they were familiar with every rock and crevice, and to the west was a bypass around the soldiers. Driving the loose horses at full run, the women and children raced toward that bypass. Yelling, but not shooting, because they had no bullets to waste, the warriors swooped down on the soldiers. It looked as though they intended to have a hand-to-hand fight with them.

Again Geronimo could not help admiring American soldiers, who never ran as Mexicans so often did but always stood their ground. However, the Apache charge was a trick.

Suddenly the racing Indians swerved east, toward some rocky hills. They rode up a narrow cleft, the only one around which horses could climb. The soldiers shot, but the range was so long that they hit no one. Reaching the summit of the cleft, the Apaches took their horses behind some rocks where they would be safe from bullets. Then they scrambled back to take up positions in the rocks themselves.

The soldiers launched a spirited attack, but they could not advance under the withering fire rained down upon them. They retreated, re-formed, and attacked again.

The Apaches shot slowly and carefully, for they wanted neither a fierce battle nor close-quarter fighting. Their only purpose was to delay the soldiers until the women and children had had time to reach a place of safety.

Two hours after the soldiers first opened

fire, the Apaches began to slip away. Each mounted his own horse, and each took a different path to rejoin the women and children. Finally only Geronimo and a dozen others were left. They fired at the soldiers and drove them to cover in the rocks. Then all the remaining Apaches rose and ran to their horses.

On their next attack, the soldiers took the hilltop. There was not an Apache left to resist them, but there were sixty different trails that led in sixty different directions.

Forty-eight hours after they left San Carlos, the Apaches crossed the Mexican border and were safe in the Sierra Madre Mountains.

CHAPTER THIRTEEN

Fortress Paradise

URGED by three of Geronimo's warriors,
fifty-three cattle climbed laboriously up a
slope and shuffled into pine forest. Stolen
from a Mexican *rancheria*, they had been
driven most of the night at the fastest pace
they could keep up. Now the cattle staggered
with weariness. But they would rest soon.

Geronimo and a warrior named Francisco,
who had helped steal the cattle, were with the
raiding party. Watching only until the cattle
had reached the mountain top, they turned
to look back down the slope.

Beneath, the Sierra Madres leveled into
low foothills. In the distance, the hills
seemed to fold into each other, so that instead
of many mountains there was just one. Finally the one was lost in a shimmering blue
haze.

The two Apaches tied their horses to nearby trees and continued to scan the hills below them. It was Geronimo who spoke.

"They come."

Far beneath, made small by distance, a line of Mexican soldiers moved slowly but steadily on the cattle's trail. The two Apaches looked at them as one might regard some interesting insects.

Geronimo had never been a chief while Apaches still lived by their ancient customs. But he was one now because he had been chosen by the people who had escaped from San Carlos, to be their leader. Neither he nor Francisco, the warrior, were the least bit excited by the sight of the Mexican soldiers. Their rifles leaned against two trees.

The Sierra Madres, with their low foot-hills that rose to ten-thousand-foot peaks, were known only to Apaches. Two hundred miles long by a hundred miles wide, the only human dwellings in the entire vast range were wickiups.

It was here that the Apaches held their pony races, played their endless games, and hunted. When they felt in need of amuse-ment or plunder, they left their camps in the Sierra Madres to raid Mexican towns or ranches. Returning to the mountains, they were always safe. No force of *rurales* had ever penetrated this wild retreat.

After a bit, Geronimo sat down and cast only an occasional glance toward the oncom-ing soldiers. He yawned.

"We needn't have been so hasty," he said. "Mexicans know two gaits, slow and slower."

"Yes," Francisco was amusing himself by tracing designs in the earth with a stick.

"Still, there are more than there were, and they come deeper into the Sierra Madres than they ever did," Geronimo said. "I am glad Loco has come with his people, and Benito, and Nana, and Mangas, and Chato, and Naiche."

Geronimo was speaking of other Apache chiefs and braves who had come to Mexico. After seeing for themselves that the American soldiers were unable to bring Whoa and Geronimo back, they, too, had defied the Army and fled the reservation. Now they, too, were living a free life in the Sierra Madre Mountains.

"We did not really need them to fight Mexicans," the sulky Francisco remarked.

"I am not so certain," Geronimo said seriously. "Have you so soon forgotten the battle we fought in the stream bed south of Arispe? It was no more than three weeks after we finally returned to the Sierra Madres. Do you remember the Mexican general who shouted my name in such foul terms?

"He said, 'That dog of a Geronimo is finally cornered!' He screamed to his soldiers that they must kill every Apache, and that he would post his wounded to shoot cowards and deserters. They were many more than we, and we might have been overwhelmed had I not shot the general."

"But you did shoot the general," Francisco pointed out.

"I did," Geronimo agreed, "and I am very glad. I have no love in my heart for Mexicans, especially Mexican generals. That is why I am happy to see so many Apaches in the Sierra Madres. Together we may fight all the Mexicans."

Francisco reminded, "We are not together."

"That is as it should be," said Geronimo. "Apaches need room, and they cannot crowd together as Mexicans and Americans do. But we may get together when we choose."

"If I had known that Chato was going raiding into Arizona, I would have chosen to ride with him," Francisco said.

Geronimo said wistfully, "I too, for I have longed to see Arizona once more and have a good fight with American soldiers."

"Let us wish Chato all success," Francisco said.

Geronimo said, "He will have it. Benito rides with him, and twenty-six picked warriors."

"Were I there, there would be twenty-seven picked warriors," Francisco bragged.

Geronimo grunted sourly and lay down to sleep. A half hour later he was awakened by Francisco's hand on his shoulder.

"They come," said Francisco.

Geronimo sat up and looked down the

slope to see some thirty soldiers climbing it. All led their horses, and they stopped often to rest. Geronimo turned to Francisco.

"These are not the *rurales* we once fought," he said. "*Rurales* never came so deeply into the Sierra Madres. If they did, they were never so foolish as to be caught in daylight on a slope such as this."

Francisco asked disinterestedly, "Who are they?"

Geronimo said, "It has come to my ears that they have been sent from a far-off place known as Mexico City. The Nan-Tan, the chief, of Mexico City has at last discovered and is greedy for the gold and silver to be found here. He has sent his soldiers to protect it. Ha!"

"Ha indeed," Francisco grunted. "Are you ready?"

"Ready," said Geronimo.

Each lifted a football-sized boulder from its bed, tilted it on end, and let it go. The rolling boulders gathered stones, gravel, more boulders. A fair-sized landslide, indeed an avalanche, thundered down. A great cloud of dust arose.

When the dust cleared, Geronimo and Francisco again saw the soldiers. They had escaped the avalanche by running frantically to one side or the other, taking their horses with them. But all were mounted now and galloping frantically back in the direction from which they had come.

Geronimo said, "The soldier chief at San Carlos asked me how we fought Mexicans. I told him bullets are too hard to get to waste on them, and that we fought them with rocks. He thought I lied."

[133]

Without another word he started up the slope, following the trail of the other three raiders and the cattle.

A week later Chato, Benito, and twenty-five of the twenty-six warriors who had gone raiding in Arizona, rode into Geronimo's camp. Chato dismounted, loosed his horse, and went to sleep beneath a pine. Benito regarded him admiringly.

"That one sleeps only in the saddle while he is on a raid!" he said. "When the rest of us slept, he stood guard!"

"Was it a good raid?" Geronimo inquired.

"A very good raid," Benito said. "For the six days we spent in Arizona, we were seldom out of the saddle. We struck where we would, and stole fresh horses where we needed them. In six days we rode four hundred and fifty miles."

Geronimo said, "I do not see Tzoe among those who returned."

"You will not see Tzoe," said Benito. "Though Chato warned him that it was a foolish thing to do, he left us and went to visit his friends who remain at San Carlos. He is now a prisoner of the white soldiers."

Geronimo staggered, as though from a

sudden blow on the head. He gasped. Though a young warrior, Tzoe had been among the loudest and fiercest in declaring that never again would he submit to the white man's rule. But he had surrendered to the same loneliness and yearning for his loved ones that was afflicting all the renegades. Who would be next?

"Is Geronimo ill?" Benito asked.

"I am not ill," Geronimo said

But he saw a dark cloud hovering over all Apaches.

CHAPTER FOURTEEN

Chief Gray Wolf

RUMOR prowled like a hunting mountain lion over the foothills of the Sierra Madres. It crept up the canyons, climbed the peaks, searched out every Apache camp, and came to Geronimo. He surrounded his camp with scouts.

The sun was four hours high when one of the scouts imitated the call of a jay. Geronimo did not stir. A jay's call meant that a friend came; a hawk's scream indicated an enemy. Ten minutes later Whoa rode into Geronimo's camp.

The huge chief of the Nedni was sweating, and Geronimo hid his wonder. He had known Whoa for many years, and had fought with him when the Kas-Kai-Ya massacre was avenged. This was the first time he had seen his friend show fear.

"Have you heard?" Whoa demanded.

Geronimo replied, "It has come to my ears that Chief Gray Wolf is in the Sierra Madres."

"He is!" Whoa exclaimed. He held up both hands with all fingers spread. "Ten times this many warriors he leads, and ten times again, and twice again! The word is that he comes in peace and only to ask Apaches to return to the reservation in Arizona. Benito believed him and let his band surrender in peace. Gray Wolf's soldiers shot the men! They cut the throats of the women and children!"

For a moment Geronimo remained silent. Ten times ten, and ten times a hundred, and twice a thousand. Not even Chief Gray Wolf, known to the white men as General George Crook, could lead two thousand soldiers into the Sierra Madres unobserved. Nor was General Crook a white chief who said one thing but meant another. He kept his promises, and he would not massacre prisoners. But it would not be well for even Geronimo to give Whoa the lie.

Finally Geronimo asked, "This you saw?"

"This I saw," said Whoa.

"You saw it with your own eyes?" Geronimo asked.

[137]

"Not with my own eyes," Whoa admitted. "One of my warriors saw."

"Name him," Geronimo said.

"It was not really one of my warriors," Whoa said. "A warrior from Naiche's camp, or Zele's, or Loco's, saw. He told my warrior."

Geronimo said, "I would live in Arizona again, if I could live as befits an Apache. I would even live on the reservation, but not on the Gila River flats."

"You would put yourself in the white man's power?" Whoa asked unbelievingly.

Geronimo said, "I put myself in no man's power. But if I might once more live in Arizona, I would keep peace with the white man and let him go his way if he kept peace and let me go mine."

"You speak madness!" Whoa gasped.

"I speak no madness," said Geronimo. "And I do not think that even Chief Gray Wolf can catch me now that I know he is here. We saw *you* coming."

"As you shall see me go," Whoa promised. "I have ridden this far to ask you to go with us."

"Whither?"

"Far to the south, where no white soldier ever has been or ever shall be," Whoa said.

Geronimo said, "I do not think I would like the south."

"I say no more," said Whoa.

Whoa caught his pony and rode away. Geronimo knew a great sorrow. Whoa was frightened. Because he feared, he was willing to see through the eyes of others rather than find out for himself how things truly were. It was indeed a sad thing.

Two days later the scout announced another friend. In twenty minutes, Ana, Benito's wife, climbed the hill to Geronimo's camp.

"Why are you here?" Geronimo demanded.

"I bear a message from Chief Gray Wolf," said Ana.

Geronimo said, "It has come to my ears that Chief Gray Wolf killed all the followers of Benito. Yet you, Benito's wife, are not dead."

"We did indeed fight some of Chief Gray Wolf's Apache scouts," said Ana. "They were commanded by the white chiefs, Crawford and Gatewood. They surprised us in our camp, and we thought they came for war. But they came for peace, and though they killed a few of us because we fought them, they took most of us prisoner and treated us very well.

"The men remain prisoners. But the children have freedom of Chief Gray Wolf's camp and all women have been sent forth with the message Chief Gray Wolf has for all Apaches. That is why I am here."

"And what is this message?" Geronimo asked.

"Return to Arizona and live in peace."

Geronimo asked, "Was Chato in Benito's camp when Gray Wolf's scouts came?"

"Chato was there," Ana said.

"And what says Chato to the message?"

"Chato and Benito have agreed to return," said Ana. "So have Zele and Naiche. I know not of the others."

"She lies," Francisco warned.

Geronimo said, "Women do not lie about their husbands. Would Chief Gray Wolf speak with me?"

"He would," said Ana.

"Where?"

Ana used a stick to trace a map on the ground. Geronimo studied it, rubbed it out with his moccasin, and nodded.

"Eat and rest," he told Ana. "Then go to Chief Gray Wolf and say Geronimo will come in four days."

In four days, carrying his Winchester repeating rifle and wearing a belt full of bullets, Geronimo approached the meeting place an hour after sunrise. He looked straight ahead only, for anything else might betray him. His warriors, who had left camp while night still held, were hidden all about. But they were to attack only if there was treachery.

Geronimo saw Captain Crawford and

Lieutenant Gatewood, army officers whose deeds had earned them the respect of all Apaches. There was Al Sieber, famed chief of scouts and one of the very few white men who could think like an Apache. Mickey Free, whom Cochise had been accused of kidnap-

ing years before, stood ready to tell Geronimo and General Crook what each said to the other. Geronimo spoke Apache, Spanish, and some English. General Crook spoke and understood English only.

Proud and haughty as the Apache himself, every inch the warrior, General Crook's eyes met Geronimo's. They did not look away.

Geronimo asked, "What would you talk about?"

"Your return to Arizona," said General Crook.

Geronimo said, "You think I will live again on the hot flats of the Gila?"

"It was not I who sent you there," said General Crook. "Choose your home. There are the White Mountains."

A mighty yearning stirred in Geronimo's heart. He was homesick for Arizona, and the White Mountains.

"What else do you ask?" Geronimo inquired.

General Crook said, "Your promise to live in peace."

"Who promises me that the white man will also keep the peace?" Geronimo asked.

"I do," said General Crook. "And have you known me to lie?"

"I have never known Chief Gray Wolf to speak falsely," Geronimo admitted. "And I see no treachery here."

Humor lighted General Crook's eyes. "How many of your warriors surround us, Geronimo?"

"Do you think I came in fear?" Geronimo asked angrily.

"I did not say that," said General Crook. "I asked how many of your warriors surround us."

"Some," Geronimo admitted. "But they are to shoot only if you start a battle."

"See for yourself that we want no battle," General Crook said. "Will you come back to live on the Apache reservation if you may choose your home in the White Mountains?"

"I will if I may do that," Geronimo said.

"Will you live in peace?"

Geronimo promised, "I will live in peace."

"When will you come?" General Crook asked.

"When I am ready."

Geronimo turned on his heel and strode away.

CHAPTER FIFTEEN

The Discontented

A MILE and a half from his farm on
Turkey Creek, in Arizona's White Mountains, Geronimo skulked in a thicket and
looked sourly at a flock of wild turkeys. They
were so many that they seemed a living car-
pet over the five-acre clearing in which they
were catching grasshoppers. But they held no
charm for Geronimo. Who besides white
men would eat a bird that ate snakes?

White men also ate the trout that swarmed
in White Mountain streams, and trout were
akin to snakes. Geronimo grimaced. He had
had enough, and more than enough, of white
men and their ways.

A lark called three times. The turkeys
skulked away. They knew that it was not a
lark calling, but a man imitating a lark. A
moment later Naiche slipped into the thicket
where Geronimo hid.

Naiche said, "No one saw me."

"It is well," said Geronimo. "Chato suspects that we are again on the point of fleeing to Mexico. He will be happy to inform the soldiers if he can discover our plans."

Naiche said, "Chato suspects everything since he turned from his own people to the white men. In his own opinion, Chato is a very great man. He told me himself that Chief Gray Wolf never would have come to the Sierra Madres if he, Chato, had not gone raiding into Arizona. He said the settlers of Arizona had decided that the Apaches would never dare leave Mexico. His raid taught them otherwise, and so Chief Gray Wolf came."

"For once, Chato spoke the truth," Geronimo said.

Without announcing himself, old Nana came so silently that neither Geronimo nor Naiche knew he was coming until he was almost upon them. Mangas and Chihuahua arrived, and the leaders who had planned this second outbreak were gathered.

Geronimo spoke. "When I met Chief Gray Wolf in Mexico, I told him that I would return to Arizona if I might live as an Apache should. But before I could come, I needed time. Not wishing to return to Arizona a poor man, I had to steal enough cattle to make me rich. My warriors and I took three hundred and fifty cattle from the Mexicans. They were honorably stolen. We brought them to Arizona when we came. But when we arrived at Fort Apache, our cattle were taken from us."

The chiefs growled like angry wolves. Geronimo continued:

"That was not what Chief Gray Wolf promised, but where is he? Where are Captain Crawford and Lieutenant Gatewood? Where are any white men we may trust? They brought us here and over us set strangers like Lieutenant Davis, who knows nothing about Apaches and cares less."

"I told Mickey Free to tell the fat white chief, Lieutenant Davis, that I had killed men before he was born!" old Nana snarled. "He cannot tell me what to do!"

Chihuahua said angrily, "He and others do tell us! We must not do this, we must not do that! But we must scratch the ground with those foolish plows they gave us, and try to grow corn when it is much easier to steal it! I promised to keep peace with white men! I never promised not to fight with and raid Papagoes and Navajos!"

"None of us promised anything except that we would live on the reservation and bother no white men," Geronimo said. "It is true that we live in the White Mountains rather than on the flats of the Gila, but how do we live? It is still better to be free and at war in Mexico than to be at peace and live like the stupid sheep which Navajo herders chase."

"Right!" Nana agreed. "It is better to die in battle than to live as a slave! Before we go, I think that I will pick a fight with the fat white chief."

"Have men, not boys, beside you if you do," Geronimo advised. "Lieutenant Davis is a warrior. How many are we?"

Naiche said, "In all, we are thirty-five

men, eight boys who know how to shoot, and a hundred and one women and children. We might have had as many more as we cared to take with us if we had been able to provide arms for them. As it is, three of the boys who can shoot must carry bows and arrows since we were unable to get enough rifles."

"It is as well," Geronimo said. "The smaller the party, the faster we may travel. We know that the Apache scouts and the white soldiers will stop us if they can. And I feel that Lieutenant Davis is suspicious."

Naiche said, "I can go to him and pick a fight. He would kill me, or I would kill him. If I killed him, he could not stop us."

"Since we are not sure he knows anything, this is not the time to fight him," Geronimo said. "He has not tried to stop us. When we are gone, he cannot stop us."

"He can send a message by the wire that talks, the telegraph," said Nana. "He can tell the soldiers at Fort Thomas to stop us, and we shall have to fight them when we meet."

Geronimo said, "If we start a fight here, we must fight all the soldiers and all the Apache scouts. If we run, we cannot be sure that we will meet anyone. It is wiser to run."

The Apaches started in late afternoon.

Geronimo was the last to leave, and he scouted thoroughly. Seeing nothing, he turned his pony southward.

Only another Apache could have hidden from Geronimo's final scouting. As soon as the runaways had gone, Mickey Free rose from the patch of brush in which he had hidden and watched every move. He ran full speed to the army headquarters and found Lieutenant Davis.

"Geronimo, Chihuahua, Mangas, and Nana lead many people toward Mexico," Mickey Free said.

Lieutenant Davis hurried to the telegraph operator.

"Send this message at once to Captain Pierce, in Fort Thomas: 'An unknown number of Apaches under Geronimo and other chiefs are fleeing toward Mexico. Head them off.'"

"Right away," the operator said.

While the operator worked his key, Lieutenant Davis tapped his foot nervously up and down. He did not as yet know how many Apaches had fled from the reservation. But he did know that, even if they were only a few, they were far more dangerous than the most savage pack of wolves that had ever roamed.

Geronimo had cut the wire with his axe

If they escaped again into the Sierra Madres, it meant more terror for the citizens of Arizona. From their stronghold in the Mexican mountains, the Apaches would certainly raid Arizona towns and ranches. It meant equal terror for Mexico, and it meant a long and costly military campaign before the runaways were again under control.

The telegraph operator continued to work his key. But Geronimo had already stopped long enough in his flight to climb one of the trees to which the telegraph wire was fastened. He had cut the wire with his axe and tied the two ends together with a piece of buckskin. This he did so that the wires would not dangle, making it easy for soldiers to find and repair the break.

After five minutes, the operator turned, much puzzled, to Lieutenant Davis.

"I cannot get through," he said.

"Stay at your key and keep trying," Lieutenant Davis said. "If you get through, say that I'm on the trail with soldiers and scouts. I hope we may catch them, but trailing will be slow at night, and I think it means another campaign in Mexico."

Lieutenant Davis was right. Geronimo and all his followers again reached Mexico and found a haven in the Sierra Madres.

CHAPTER SIXTEEN

Hunted Like Wolves

GERONIMO galloped wildly through the black night. Naiche rode beside him. Ten of the eighteen warriors who remained with Geronimo followed.

Geronimo turned his head. He saw light from the burning buildings of the Arizona ranch that he and his warriors had just raided, reflected in the sky. The Apaches had taken fresh horses. But the four men who had been at the ranch had fled after firing a few shots.

Presently Geronimo pulled in his horse to a trot. The rest slowed. Naiche drew in nearer to his chief.

"I wish that the white men had stayed to fight," he said.

"I too," said Geronimo, "but the white men are not fools. They remain great liars.

The last time, I raided in Arizona with but six men, and Kieta deserted to return to San Carlos. But the white men said we had two hundred warriors. Loco, who remains on the reservation, sent me a messenger, asking to know where we found such strength."

Naiche asked anxiously, "Was that the whole message?"

"There was no more," Geronimo said.

Said Naiche, "Then I am sad. My wife and children are in Arizona. My relatives are there. I am sorely in need of news of them.

Why does Chihuahua send me no word? He returned to the reservation the second time Chief Gray Wolf came to us and asked us to come in."

"There is no knowing what happened to Chihuahua," Geronimo said. "Chief Gray Wolf has gone from Arizona, and the Apaches will never see him again."

General Crook had indeed made a second journey to Mexico, and again he met the runaway Apaches and tried to persuade them to come back to the reservation. Chihuahua and his followers had returned. Mangas and two or three others had fled deeper into Mexico, but Geronimo and Naiche had promised to return. At the last minute they, with eighteen other men and nineteen women and children, had changed their minds and fled back into the Sierra Madres.

General Crook had been sharply rebuked by his commander for letting Geronimo escape. So he had asked to be relieved of duty in Arizona and sent back to Texas. His wish was granted, and a general named Miles had come to Arizona to take his place.

General Miles had five thousand soldiers at his command, and their principal duty was to capture Geronimo. A large number of

Mexican *rurales* and police were afield for the same purpose. Besides these, there were many ranchers, cowboys, miners, and townsmen who would gladly do anything they could to put an end to Geronimo and his followers. There were certainly at least ten thousand people actively plotting the downfall of this one Apache chief.

And not all of them together had come near to succeeding.

By special arrangement with Mexico, American troops were permitted to range south of the border, and there had been several fights between them and Geronimo's band. Some American soldiers had been killed or wounded, and the Mexicans has suffered too. But Geronimo had not lost a single warrior. Not one of his followers had even been wounded. Yet the Apache chief was discouraged.

He swayed in the saddle, and bright lights flashed before his eyes. He put a hand in front of his eyes to shut out the lights.

"Are you ill?" Naiche asked in alarm.

"I am tired," said Geronimo.

Naiche said, "We may stop and rest."

"I speak not of body weariness," Geronimo said. "My spirit is tired."

"I understand," said Naiche. "We have fought for a very long while. We have been driven from our camps and our cooking fires. Seven times in fifteen months we lost all our horses and had to steal more. We know not when we will have to fight many soldiers. The spirits of all of us are tired, but we dare not surrender."

"We dare not," Geronimo agreed. "Chief Gray Wolf is gone. Captain Crawford is dead. Lieutenant Gatewood is gone. There is not one white man among all who pursue us whom we may trust. Almost I wish that I had gone in with Chief Gray Wolf."

"I too," Naiche murmured.

They halted at daylight in a rockbound little canyon. Horses that had become both weary and thirsty stood with heads raised and nostrils flared. They smelled water, for there was a water hole ahead. But the warriors tied their mounts and waited.

Carrying his Winchester repeating rifle, Geronimo slipped off alone. With no more fuss than a slinking coyote, he made his way among the boulders and the scrawny little trees that grew between them.

After a bit Geronimo stopped and cut a number of leafy twigs. He thrust them into his headband so that, if he held very still, whoever saw him would think they saw a bush instead. Then he dropped to wriggle forward on his stomach. Presently he looked down into another canyon.

The water hole was there, and the water was fresh and cold. Green grass surrounded it. Great cottonwood trees bordered it. But a herd of horses browsed on the grass, and pack mules stamped at a picket line. There were packs and tents, and there were more than twenty soldiers whose only reason for being here was to keep Geronimo away from the water.

Geronimo slipped away as quietly as he had come.

"Soldiers await," he told Naiche when he had returned to his warriors.

"Many soldiers?" Naiche asked.

"Too many for us to fight," Geronimo said.

Naiche said, "Then we must go."

"No. We must loose our horses," said Geronimo.

Naiche said, "They will run to water."

"They will run to water," Geronimo agreed.

Naiche asked wonderingly, "You would give good horses to white soldiers?"

"These horses are too spent to serve us any longer," Geronimo said. "Let them go."

Tie ropes were slipped. Following the smell of water, the horses were off at a gallop.

Geronimo led his warriors forward. He stopped them just beneath the rim of the canyon in which the water hole lay. Again he thrust bits of brush into his headband and crawled forward to look.

The thirsty horses had come in and were crowding each other at the water hole. A young lieutenant was ordering his men to mount. A scout whom Geronimo had seen, but whose name he had never heard, was arguing with the lieutenant.

"Don't do it!" the scout said. "Don't do it, Lieutenant!"

"You say these horses were loosed by Geronimo's men?" the lieutenant asked.

The scout said, "Couldn't of been nobody else, an' every horse wears the Pratt brand. Geronimo must of stole them there. I figure we'll find the Pratt ranch burned an' maybe the Pratt brothers dead. But don't dash off in all directions thisaway."

"If Geronimo's lost his horses, he and his men are afoot!" the young lieutenant exclaimed.

"The only horses Geronimo ever *lost* was them our scouts or soldiers took away from him," the scout said. "He's turned these loose for some deviltry of his own. An' did you ever try to hunt Apaches when they was afoot?"

"No," the lieutenant admitted. "But they should be easy to catch."

" 'Bout as easy as so many quail with six extry wings," the scout said. "You can't catch 'em."

The lieutenant said sternly, "Mount and come with us."

"All right," the scout said. "But don't leave no horses here!"

"I won't. But we must travel fast so I'll leave the pack mules."

"Then leave a guard too."

"I'll need every man," the lieutenant said.

"S'pose the Apaches come here?" the scout asked.

"They won't," the lieutenant said. "They're too cowardly. Geronimo and every last one of his men are running for Mexico. We must overtake them. Geronimo's the last Apache war chief! When he's captured or killed, it will mean an end to Indian wars here in the Southwest! The least I'll get out of this is a captain's rating, and perhaps even a major's!"

The scout said, "If I'm asked, I'll say I told you 'twas a fool thing to do."

"Say what you please," the lieutenant said. "I know what I'm doing."

The soldiers followed the scout, who in turn followed the back trail of the horses. When they found the place where the horses had been loosed, the lieutenant thought, they would also find helpless Apaches on foot.

When the soldiers were out of sight, Geronimo signaled his men forward.

They drank at the water hole. Then they rummaged hastily through the packs and tents and took all the rifles and ammunition they could find. Minutes later, each warrior was mounted on a mule. Geronimo led them into rough and rocky ground where mules could travel but horses could not.

Long before the young lieutenant brought his men back to their camp, every Apache was safe.

CHAPTER SEVENTEEN

A Gallant Soldier

SITTING in the shade of some pines on the rim of a lofty mountain, Geronimo stared down at Mexico's Bavispe River. From the mountain top the river looked like a silver ribbon that followed the curves of the valley and gave back the sparkle of the sun.

Geronimo shook his head. When he was a medicine man, he had tried in vain to see the visions that should appear to all *shamans*. Though he was no longer a *shaman*, visions came now.

He saw that long past day when he had stolen Delgadito's war horse to fight a duel of stallions with the son of Ponce. Again he went with Delgadito on the raid, and saw the two Papagoes who had come to steal horses. Once more he lived in his mother's wickiup, and knew the love that had warmed him there. Next followed his happy days with Alope, but not the massacre at Kas-Kai-Ya.

Then the battle that avenged the massacre, the ambush of the California Volunteers in Apache Pass, and the battles that had been since.

He thought of all that had passed since his first fight with the two Papagoes. Geronimo had been twelve years old then. He was fifty-eight now. He had known forty-six years of war.

More visions came. Geronimo saw old Mangus Coloradus, leaving the Mimbreno village to surrender to the white man. He saw

Cochise, who fought fiercely for ten years after the death of Mangus Coloradus but finally gave in too.

No more visions appeared. Geronimo turned to Naiche, who sat beside him.

"You told me that you long to see your wife, your children, your relatives," he said.

"I do," said Naiche. "Have you no wish again to visit your blood kin?"

"No one awaits me—"

Geronimo was interrupted by the whistle of a hawk, the sentry's signal that an enemy came. The sentry signaled again, the enemy was not in force.

The women and children ran to hurry the horses into hiding. The men hid themselves where they could ambush their foe. In less than a half minute, not one of Geronimo's band and no horses could be seen.

Presently two Apaches appeared. One was Kieta, who had deserted Geronimo while raiding in Arizona. The second was a warrior named Martine.

When the pair was well within the ambush, Geronimo and his hidden warriors sprang up. Kieta and Martine stood motionless. But both knew that, if either raised a weapon, both would die.

[165]

Geronimo said, "It is good to see you again, Kieta."

"I am here because I like you, Geronimo," Kieta said, "and I like you because you led us well. I know you bear me no ill will because I left you and returned to San Carlos."

Said Geronimo, "If you wished to follow me no more, your own path was before you, and how can I bear ill will because you chose it? Have you now returned to me and brought Martine with you?"

"We are here as messengers for a very gallant soldier," Kieta said.

Geronimo said harshly, "I treat with no soldiers."

"Will you hear his name?" Kieta asked.

Geronimo said, "I will hear his name."

"Lieutenant Gatewood," said Kieta.

Geronimo could not hide his astonishment. He knew that Lieutenant Gatewood was fierce in battle, merciful in victory, and always true to his word. With that respect which one great warrior must feel for another, Geronimo said, "More than once I have met Lieutenant Gatewood in battle. But it came to my ears that he had gone far from the land of the Apaches."

"Your ears heard truly," Kieta said. "Lieutenant Gatewood has been in a place so far off that I do not even know its name. But when he learned that Geronimo refuses even to talk with the soldiers who are pursuing him, he came as one whom Geronimo himself knows he may trust."

"How many soldiers are with him?" Geronimo asked.

Kieta said, "There are six soldiers, all of whom serve as couriers and none as warriors. There are two interpreters, Jose Maria and Tom Horn."

"They are all?" Geronimo asked.

"They are all with Lieutenant Gatewood," said Kieta. "But there are many soldiers not far away. Will you talk with this brave man?"

Geronimo gave himself to serious thought. After a while, he looked at Kieta.

"I will talk with him," he said. "But only Lieutenant Gatewood, the six couriers, and Tom Horn and Jose Maria. No one else must come to the meeting place. Should there be soldiers, we fight."

"We go to tell him," Kieta said.

Geronimo said, "Martine goes to tell him. Just to be sure Martine speaks truly, you stay with us until he returns."

Later Geronimo stood very still as he watched Lieutenant Gatewood and his group come near. Lieutenant Gatewood had been ill and showed it. But he was armed as a warrior should be, and mounted as a warrior should be, and he was completely at ease. True to his word, he was accompanied only by the six couriers and two interpreters.

Geronimo's mind took him back almost six years to a nameless canyon. He and Naiche, with a large band of well-armed warriors, had succeeded in luring a company of United States Cavalry to a water hole in the canyon. The Apaches fell upon the soldiers and might have massacred every one had not the brave Lieutenant Gatewood rallied his men and led them out of the trap.

Geronimo stirred uneasily. His warriors could kill these few men in less than a minute. But even as the thought occurred to him, he knew that he would never give the order to shoot. Not when this gallant soldier was in command.

CHAPTER EIGHTEEN

The Last Surrender

LIEUTENANT GATEWOOD dismounted, handed the reins of his horse to one of the couriers, and shook hands with Geronimo. Geronimo searched the officer's face for some sign of fear. But there was not even a slight nervousness. Lieutenant Gatewood was indeed worthy of his reputation for both courage and gallantry.

Geronimo said, "Your face is pale and drawn, as though it has not seen the sun in too many days. Or perhaps you have been ill?"

"It is nothing," said Lieutenant Gatewood. "I have merely ridden far and fast so that I may talk with Geronimo."

"You did not say, 'My friend, Geronimo,'" Geronimo pointed out.

"You are not my friend," Lieutenant Gatewood said calmly. "You are the friend of no white man or Mexican as long as you continue to live like a wild beast, and raid and kill at your pleasure. Except for those who are with you now, even the Apaches have turned against you, for you have given a bad name to Apaches who would live at peace."

"It is true that many thirst for my blood," Geronimo said thoughtfully. "It is equally true that you still speak with a straight tongue. Some have called me 'friend,' and when they thought I was no longer suspicious, have tried to betray me. But you say at once that you are not my friend, and that is honest talk. What would you have from me?"

Lieutenant Gatewood said, "For myself I want nothing, and as a soldier I may ask nothing. But for General Miles, the great chief in command of the soldiers who are pursuing you, I ask your surrender and the surrender of all your band."

Geronimo asked, "And what does General Miles offer in return?"

"Imprisonment in Florida for you and your families," Lieutenant Gatewood said.

"Is he mad?" Geronimo flared angrily. "His soldiers have pursued me for many months, and we have fought them many times. Many soldiers have died in these fights, but

[*171*]

not a single Apache has been killed by white soldiers. Does your General Miles not know that we are capable of carrying on the fight?"

"He knows," Lieutenant Gatewood said. "But if you fail to surrender, General Miles has another offer. He will hunt you down and kill every one of you if it takes another fifty years."

"Take a message to your General Miles," Geronimo said. "Tell him that we will return to Arizona if we may go back to our homes in the White Mountains, and if we may live there as we did before fleeing into Mexico."

"That is childish talk, Geronimo," Lieutenant Gatewood said. "You have had many opportunities to prove that you would live in peace on the reservation. There will not be another chance. General Miles' orders stand. Accept imprisonment in Florida or be killed by soldiers."

"We may also kill soldiers," Geronimo reminded him.

"That you have proven many times," Lieutenant Gatewood admitted. "But you remember the times of long ago, when for every white man in Arizona there were a hundred Apaches. Now, for every Apache, there are two hundred white men and more to come. You cannot kill all the soldiers."

"Nor can they kill us," Geronimo said. "My terms stand. We return to the White Mountains and live as we once lived, or we continue the war."

Lieutenant Gatewood turned suddenly to Naiche and smiled. "I saw your mother and daughter, Naiche, just after they came in with Chihuahua's band. They have been sent to Florida with the rest, but both inquired about you."

"Are they well?" Naiche asked eagerly.

"Very well," Lieutenant Gatewood said. "They wish you to surrender so that you may join them, and I am to remind you than an enemy more merciless than any soldiers lies in wait. It is winter that is just ahead. Geronimo, do I have your final answer?"

Geronimo said, "May we talk again tomorrow?"

"We may," said Lieutenant Gatewood.

They parted. Lieutenant Gatewood and his party returned to their camp while the Apaches went to theirs. The Indians were sober and thoughtful.

"It is true," Geronimo said, "that few animals have been hunted harder than we. We have fought and fought well, but we are very few, and our enemies are very many. We cannot continue to fight them forever."

Said Naiche, "It is also true that we would like to see our friends and families again. There is small chance of doing that as long we are in Mexico and they are in Florida."

Others of the band murmured agreement. All were desperately tired and lonely. They had endured far more than flesh and blood should be expected to bear. But they were willing to continue the fight if Geronimo and Naiche decided that that was best.

"Yet," Naiche continued, "I fear to surrender even more than I fear to continue the battle. Mexicans south of the border and Americans north of it would kill us as readily as we would kill a pack of rabid wolves. If we hand our arms over to Lieutenant Gatewood, who will protect us until we are safe in Florida?"

Suddenly Geronimo, who had been silent, saw in full the vision he had seen only in part as he sat beside Naiche. There was old Mangus Coloradus advising his people to make peace with the white men, since they could never hope to conquer them. There was Cochise, who had needed ten years of bloody war to teach him what Mangus Coloradus had been taught by his own wisdom. Now, almost twenty-five years after the death of Mangus Coloradus, Geronimo finally understood what one of these chiefs had known and the other had learned.

Apaches could not fight the white men. But neither could they surrender to them unless it was possible to work out a plan guaranteeing their own safety.

When they resumed their talks the next day, Geronimo said bluntly to Lieutenant Gatewood, "Forget you are a white man and pretend you are one of us. What would you do?"

"Trust General Miles and surrender to him," Lieutenant Gatewood said promptly.

[*175*]

"So you have spoken and so shall we do," said Geronimo. "But it is a long way to the border where General Miles awaits, and this is enemy country. We will not surrender our arms until we are met by General Miles."

"That is agreeable," said Lieutenant Gatewood. "In addition, Captain Lawton and a company of soldiers are camped not far away. I will ask them to march with you and help beat off any Mexicans who may attack."

"You march with us," Geronimo said.

"Captain Lawton and his soldiers may come, but they are to stay ahead or behind. We do not care to mingle with white soldiers."

"That, too, is agreeable," said Lieutenant Gatewood.

It was thus that the Apaches marched to the border of Mexico. Lieutenant Gatewood marched with them. Captain Lawton provided an escort of American soldiers. And a mob of two hundred Mexicans, who finally saw the hated Apaches in captivity, trailed

them all the way. But the Mexicans did not dare start a fight.

When they reached the camp where General Miles was waiting, Geronimo stalked haughtily to the general, who stared coldly at the great Apache leader. Geronimo and his warriors laid down the arms that they had carried so many miles and into so many battles. The disarmed Apaches were surrounded by soldiers who took them, first to prison cells at Arizona's Fort Bowie, then to the train that carried them to exile in Florida.

So ended the fighting days of Geronimo, the last and fiercest Apache war chief. And so, also, ended the Indian Wars in the Southwest. Never again would men and women on lonely ranches or in isolated villages awaken, trembling, in the middle of the night to hear the pound of ponies' hoofs and the wild Apache war cry. Never again would travelers in Arizona, New Mexico, and northern Mexico find it necessary to travel in groups and well-armed for fear of Apache attacks.

Geronimo and his followers, as well as many other Chiricahua and Warm Springs Apaches, were imprisoned at old Fort Pickens, or at Fort Marion, in Florida. Eventually they were moved to a reservation in what was then

Indian Territory and what is now the State of Oklahoma. There Geronimo died at Fort Sill, on February 17, 1909.

Whether he was a great villain or a great patriot depends on whether one looks at him with the eyes of the white men whom he plundered, or the Apaches whom he championed. But nobody can deny that he fought for a free life for himself and his people and that he was one of the greatest warriors of all time.

About the Author

JIM KJELGAARD was born in New York City but spent his childhood and youth in the Pennsylvania mountains. There he learned to hunt, fish, and handle dogs. He still likes to hunt and has done so in most parts of the United States and Canada, although he has exchanged his rifles and shotguns for cameras. After graduating from high school, he spent two years at Syracuse University Extension. Since then he has held a variety of jobs ranging all the way from trapper to factory superintendent, and has been writing professionally for over twenty years. Of some thirty successful books, all but one are for young people.

About the Artist

CHARLES BANKS WILSON, well known to young people for his illustrations of many historical books about the West, has achieved equal success as a painter. Over 150 exhibitions of his work have been held in museums throughout America. In both book illustration and painting, Mr. Wilson is associated with the contemporary life of the American Indian. Many Indian ceremonials which have never been photographed are recorded in his work, which has taken him throughout the Southwest as well as the Far West. He lives in his native Oklahoma with his wife, a Quapaw Indian princess, and their two children. Since 1947 he has been head of the Art Department of the Northeastern Oklahoma A. & M. College.

Signature Books

"Names That Made History"

ENID LAMONTE MEADOWCROFT, *Supervising Editor*

THE STORY OF ANDREW JACKSON
By Enid LaMonte Meadowcroft. *Illustrated by David Hendrickson*
THE STORY OF THOMAS JEFFERSON
By Earl Schenck Miers. *Illustrated by Reynold C. Pollak*
THE STORY OF JOAN OF ARC
By Jeannette Covert Nolan. *Illustrated by Pranas Lapé*
THE STORY OF JOHN PAUL JONES
By Iris Vinton. *Illustrated by Edward A. Wilson*
THE STORY OF HELEN KELLER
By Lorena A. Hickok. *Illustrated by Jo Polseno*
THE STORY OF JACQUELINE KENNEDY
By Alida Sims Malkus *Illustrated by Michael Lowenbein*
THE STORY OF PRESIDENT KENNEDY
By Iris Vinton. *Illustrated by Carl C. Cassler*
THE STORY OF LAFAYETTE
By Hazel Wilson. *Illustrated by Edy Legrand*
THE STORY OF ROBERT E. LEE
By Iris Vinton. *Illustrated by John Alan Maxwell*
THE STORY OF ABRAHAM LINCOLN
By Nina Brown Baker. *Illustrated by Warren Baumgartner*
THE STORY OF MOZART
By Helen L. Kaufmann. *Illustrated by Eric M. Simon*
THE STORY OF FLORENCE NIGHTINGALE
By Margaret Leighton. *Illustrated by Corinne B. Dillon*
THE STORY OF ANNIE OAKLEY
By Edmund Collier. *Illustrated by Leon Gregori*
THE STORY OF LOUIS PASTEUR
By Alida Sims Malkus. *Illustrated by Jo Spier*
THE STORY OF POCAHONTAS
By Shirley Graham. *Illustrated by Mario Cooper*
THE STORY OF MARCO POLO
By Olive Price. *Illustrated by Federico Castellon*
THE STORY OF ELEANOR ROOSEVELT
By Lorena A. Hickok. *Illustrated by William Barss*
THE STORY OF FRANKLIN D. ROOSEVELT
By Lorena A. Hickok. *Illustrated by Leonard Vosburgh*
THE STORY OF THEODORE ROOSEVELT
By Winthrop Neilson. *Illustrated by Edward A. Wilson*
THE STORY OF ROBERT LOUIS STEVENSON
By Joan Howard. *Illustrated by Jo Polseno*
THE STORY OF MARK TWAIN
By Joan Howard. *Illustrated by Donald McKay*
THE STORY OF GEORGE WASHINGTON
By Enid LaMonte Meadowcroft. *Illustrated by Edward A. Wilson*
THE STORY OF MARTHA WASHINGTON
By Jeannette Covert Nolan. *Illustrated by Corinne B. Dillon*
THE STORY OF MAD ANTHONY WAYNE
By Hazel Wilson. *Illustrated by Lawrence Beall Smith*
